Report from Paradise

REPORT
FROM PARADISE

BY MARK TWAIN

WITH DRAWINGS BY
CHARLES LOCKE

HARPER & BROTHERS PUBLISHERS
NEW YORK / 1952

FIRST EDITION

F-B

Contents

Report from Paradise · Introduction

A NY BOOK WHICH CAN INCREASE OUR KNOWLEDGE OF OUR FINAL HOME SHOULD BE WELCOME," DRYLY WROTE Mark Twain in a never-published review of George Woodward Warder's book *The Cities of the Sun*, in 1901. He could not resist some satiric thrusts at this fellow-Missourian's cocksure knowledge of celestial geography, for Mr. Warder had boldly located St. John's New Jerusalem within the flaming mass of the sun itself. Not only had he "added the modern improvements" but made the city limits embrace an area three-quarters the size of continental United States. This last detail Mark Twain applauded. Enlarging heaven to make room for billions, not just an elite corps of sectarians, always appealed to him.

Mr. Warder has opened my eyes to the mighty dimensions of the New Jerusalem [he wrote], and for this service I am his obliged debtor ... I suddenly see the little New Jerusalem expand and cover a continent, and lift its soaring masses skyward up and up, hundreds of miles, and fade twinkling out in remoteness beyond the reach of human vision! ...

It makes one's mouth water. It would be a wonderful experience to stand there in those enchanted surroundings and hear Shakespeare and Milton and Bunyan read from their noble works. And it might be that they would like to hear me read some of my things. No, it could never be; they would not care for me. They would not know me, they would not understand me, and they would say they had an engagement. But if I could only be there, and walk about and

ix

look, and listen, I should be satisfied and not make a noise. My life is fading to its close, and someday I shall know.[1]

Fittingly enough, the last book Mark Twain published, in October 1909, six months before his death, was his own fantasy of the life to come, called *Extract from Captain Stormfield's Visit to Heaven*.

It was not however the child of his sunset years, but in conception one of his youngest books. Its seed had been sown forty-three years before. A fledgling lecturer and humorist of San Francisco, Samuel Clemens in search of national fame and fortune had taken passage on December 15, 1866, on the steamship *America*, Captain Edgar Wakeman. Soon after clearing the Golden Gate, on the first night out they ran into terrific weather. The storm splintered about twenty feet of the bulwarks forward and flooded the steerage. While some fell to praying for the ship, a seasoned traveler took solace in a more proximate providence: "If anybody can save her it's old Wakeman." So young Clemens recorded in his notebook.

With this crisis past, the ex-Mississippi pilot quickly scraped an acquaintance with this still more experienced navigator—robust, with coal-black hair and beard, weather tanned, and tattooed as garishly as a South Sea idol, ruling his crew with "the kind of eye which men obey without talking back." He was an honest and simple soul, with the dammed-up communicativeness of a lonely wayfaring man. No lover of the bottle or gaming table, he loved to pass the time by telling favored passengers yarns of the sea, the kind

[1]Manuscript in the Mark Twain Papers.

of stories that seldom refrained from testing the tensile strength of facts.

His tale about the fabulous rats that left a doomed ship appeared over Mark Twain's signature in the *Alta California* of February 24, 1867, ascribed to a "Captain Waxman." Later, when he came to write *Roughing It*, Clemens told how Wakeman, now called "Captain Ned Blakely," with no help from the law once arrested a bully in the Chincha Islands who had murdered the Captain's Negro mate, grudgingly agreed to the motions of a trial, but reserved the exclusive pleasure of hanging the culprit with his own hands after dinning into his ears four random chapters from the Bible. Still later, in preparing "Rambling Notes of an Idle Excursion" about a trip to Bermuda in 1877 with his clerical crony Joe Twichell, Mark Twain recalled how Twichell, traveling incognito, had once encountered "Captain Hurricane Jones," the same old seadog, who rationally explained all the Old Testament miracles to him.

For Wakeman—who, when out of earshot of ladies, frequently resorted to an idiom edged with brimstone and illumined by the lightning of blasphemy—was a great Bible reader and self-taught expounder of the Holy Book. He had somehow assimilated all its supernaturalism to his own simple, kindly, forthright realism. In fact, he was an inexhaustible source of good "copy," and long before they had reached the Isthmus on this first run Clemens reflected in his journal that "I'd rather travel with that old portly, hearty, jolly, boisterous, good-natured sailor, Capt. Ned Wakeman, than any other man I ever came across."

On his return voyage to California in 1868 Mark Twain

had the good luck to travel with Wakeman again, and the Captain told him about a still more extraordinary experience, "a visit which he had made to heaven." To the Captain it was all so vivid that it had long ceased to be a dream. As Mark Twain recollected the circumstances many years later, in dictating his autobiography in 1906, "I kept it in my mind, and a month or two later I put it on paper—this was the first quarter of 1868, I think." The first draft that survives, written on the Crystal Lake Mills stationery and with the gorgeous purple ink he often employed in the middle years, dates probably from the 1870's.

Originally its hero was named "Cap'n Hurricane Jones," as in the Bermuda sketch, because of the epic rages for which Wakeman was celebrated. "When his temper was up," wrote the Captain's admirer, "he performed all the functions of an earthquake, without the noise." But this name has been methodically crossed out and "Stormfield" substituted, more subtly suggesting the same idea. So well did Mark Twain like the new name that he gave it to the house at Redding, Connecticut, into which he moved in 1908, after the summer thunderstorms came. He had also used it some years before in an unpublished fragment—a novel with a hapless plot about erecting a monument to Adam, father of the human race—whose chief character, a generous and eccentric naval officer, is clearly an elder reincarnation of Wakeman.

In fact, under various names and plot situations, old Ned Wakeman walked through Mark Twain's dreamworld for the rest of that author's life, among a motley band of favorites that included Tom and Huck and Nigger Jim, Adam and Eve, Satan, and Noah.

xii

For it was not the bluff old sea captain alone but his dream that stirred Clemens's imagination. The son of a small-town agnostic lawyer and a Presbyterian mother, Mark Twain inherited the will to disbelieve, but also a lifelong fascination with the mythology taught at Hannibal's Old Ship of Zion Sunday school. "I don't believe in hell—but I'm afraid of it," he said in later years. Similarly he didn't believe in heaven, but was powerfully attracted to it—if for no other purpose than to explode the orthodoxies of those who claimed it as their monopoly.

To describe heaven and the voyage thither through the eyes of a simple old sailor with a flair for Biblical exegesis struck him from the start as a good idea. It came to him in 1868, when the national best seller happened to be a novel called *The Gates Ajar*, by Elizabeth Stuart Phelps, a psychic New England girl who had lost her lover in the Civil War. It appealed to thousands of others who had suffered similar losses and were not overcritical of the saccharine and sentimental Paradise she presented. Furthermore, as Mark Twain recalled long afterwards, Miss Phelps "had imagined a mean little ten-cent heaven about the size of Rhode Island." His reaction was to describe a heaven measured in millions of miles. Some time later, when Clemens came to talk the language of Fizeau and Foucault, of Michelson and Morley, he found a better yardstick in the light year, "without doubt the most stupendous and impressive phrase that exists in any language," he reflected in 1906.[2]

2 *Mark Twain in Eruption*, 247 n. An unpublished and mediocre segment of *Stormfield* among the Mark Twain Papers relates a dialogue between the Captain and his angelic pal Sandy on the subject of astronomy, largely by hearsay from Professor Higgins, who "used to be astronomical professor of astronomy at Harvard." Stag-

The physical insignificance of our planet, known celestially as "the Wart," finds its counterpart in the equally absurd cosmic egotism of man. A child of nineteenth-century science, Mark Twain rejoiced in the growth of knowledge which had exploded old-fashioned notions about an earth-centered universe or even a heliocentric one. Plato (in the *Timaeus*), Fénelon, Locke, Newton, Shaftesbury and others had yearned for this liberation in thought, but it remained for modern astronomy to achieve it. At least by report Clemens knew these things, and they early became part and parcel of his philosophy.

If heaven existed, Mark Twain felt sure that conventional ideas about it were mostly bosh. He shared Huck Finn's attitude after Miss Watson told him "all about the good place. She said all a body would have to do there was to go around all day long with a harp and sing, forever and ever. So I didn't think much of it." Captain Stormfield, who knows only a single tune, finds that hymn-singing palls within a few minutes, not to mention eternity, while haloes and palm branches soon get to be an encumbrance and a nuisance. After all, they are issued from the wardrobe of heaven only because the pious arrive clamoring for them. In an eleven-page passage, which Mark finally jettisoned from the printed

gered by the concept of light years and the vast emptiness of interstellar space ("This heaven ain't built on any 'Gates Ajar' proportions"), the two cronies go off looking for an "asterisk" (asteroid) and discover a Lilliputian world having all the complacencies of earth: "These people had a quite good opinion of themselves, although they were no bigger than a banana, and many of them no bigger than a clothes pin. In church it was a common thing for the preacher to look out over his congregation and speak of them as the noblest work of God—and never a clothes pin smiled! These little animals were having wars all the time, and raising armies and building navies, and striving after the approval of God every way they could."

version, he went more fully into a topic broached at the start of Chapter IV, the Captain's awkward attempts to fly. Again and again the wind upsets his reckonings, landing him a-sprawl in the briers. Reasoning that birds handle their wings better because they have a rudder, the Captain plucks out a fistful of feathers and fastens them on behind.

They were not part of me, and I couldn't work them, they only just stuck out behind in a foolish bunch like a feather-duster and didn't do any good. And then some boys came along and one of them said,—

"Oh, here's fun! Here's an angel with a tail. Let's clod him."

They did clod me, too, and I had to fly into some woods a mile off to get away from them.

In disgust, he says, "I rolled up my wings in an old last week's *Zion Herald,* and tucked them away in the pantry."

If heaven is not perpetual hosannahs, neither is it pure unadulterated bliss. Believing in the relativity of happiness —that happiness is essentially relief from unhappiness— Mark Twain allows for celestial pain and suffering, though both are short-lived. Another discarded fragment, four pages long, dwells upon this point as raised at the close of the third chapter. An instance is the shock of a newly-arrived mother who finds her long-lost child grown to adulthood in heaven—a parent obviously devoted to "momism" who bitterly resents the child's right to grow up. The revised version is probably an improvement, save that one misses the bereaved mother's speedy consolation for having no baby to dandle:

"She has raked up twenty or thirty friends and relations who died within two or three years before she did, and it would have done your heart good to see these old cronies meet again. She has raked up her husband, too—he died about five years ahead of her. Happy? there ain't anybody in these realms that is happier than Mrs. Foster. She has got acquainted with a lot of simple-minded, harmless, Jersey people,—regular gossips—and they get together every day and pull other people's reputations to pieces, and slander the elect in general, wholesale and retail, and have a noble good time. Much she will be bothering about her lost child a month from now!"

"No, but do they really deal in that kind of gossip in heaven?"

"How you talk! Would heaven be heaven if you couldn't slander folks?"

"Come to think, I don't believe it would—for some people—but I hadn't thought of it before."

"For 'some people.' There you hit it. The trouble on earth is, that they leave out the *some people* class—they try to fix up a heaven for only one kind of people. It won't work. There's all kinds here—and God cares for all kinds. He makes all happy: if he can't do it in one way, he does it in another. He doesn't leave anybody out in the cold."[3]

Mark Twain's heaven was devised, at least in part, for purposes of satire. It is all-embracing, to show up the petti-

[3] From the manuscript owned by the American Academy of Arts and Letters, here quoted by kind permission of that institution. This manuscript bears a title page written in the hand of Mark Twain's friend and biographer Albert Bigelow Paine, which serves incidentally to identify the "Peters" repeatedly addressed by the narrator in Chapter III, below:

"Travels of Capt. Eli Stormfield, Mariner in Heaven,
Taken down from his own Lips by
Rev. George H. Peters, of Marysville, Calif."

Clemens's anecdote in "Rambling Notes" about Captain Hurricane Jones gives Twichell the name of "the Rev. Mr. Peters."

ness of sectarians, and also a social hierarchy, to confute the self-important. A place where the inheritors of unfulfilled renown come into their own, it honors a poor Tennessee tailor whose natural gifts for poetry excelled Shakespeare's, a Boston bricklayer whose military gift exceeded Caesar's, and a Hoboken sausage-maker who stealthily fed the poor while gaining the reputation of a miser. This romantic idea goes back at least to Gray's *Elegy* and its "mute inglorious Miltons." Mark Twain plainly gained satisfaction from forecasting the arrival of "a Brooklyn preacher by the name of Talmage" who had avowed in sermons "that the first thing he does when he gets to heaven will be to fling his arms around Abraham, Isaac and Jacob, and kiss them and weep on them." But, as the Captain's experienced friend assures him, this preacher will find he is very small potatoes beside such dignitaries. The Reverend T. DeWitt Talmage, pastor of Brooklyn's Central Presbyterian Church (later Tabernacle), fashionable pulpit orator, had been a passing target for Mark Twain's satire in 1870, for having said that the odor of workingmen among his congregation was offensive to more genteel nostrils. In columns of the Buffalo *Express*, of which Clemens was then co-owner, and a monthly department which he conducted for the *Galaxy*, Mark Twain let fly at that gratuitous bit of clerical snobbery. This stratum in the Stormfield deposit almost certainly belongs to about the same phase. It was retained when publication finally occurred, even though Talmage meanwhile had been translated by death in 1902.

This clue is one of several that disclose how long Mark Twain kept the unfinished story beside him. To his brother

Orion on March 23, 1878 he recalled how he had "mapped out my 'Journey in Heaven' nine years ago," and after mulling over it a year or so had written it up. Unsatisfied, he let it lie fallow till about 1873, then tackled it again and showed the results to Howells. That friend advised publication, but recommended an indorsement (if possible) from the English divine Dean Stanley, to "draw some of the teeth of the religious press," but this fanciful proposal was scrapped. However, Clemens did not intend deliberately to grate upon religious sensibilities. "Neither Howells nor I believe in hell or the divinity of the Savior," he wrote his brother, "but no matter, the Savior is none the less a sacred Personage, and a man should have no desire or disposition to refer to him lightly, profanely, or otherwise than with the profoundest reverence." No portion of the Stormfield cycle, published or unpublished, invokes the presence of God, although an unprinted fragment about the creation of Man—as witnessed by an angel named Slattery—refers with elaborate circumlocution to "the Authorities."[4] The only allusion to Christ is unexceptionable, when to the puzzled head clerk Stormfield seeks to identify his world as "the one the Savior saved."

He bent his head at the Name. Then he says, gently—
"The worlds He has saved are like the gates of heaven in number—none can count them."

Another question in taste concerned the possibility of having Stormfield explore the nether regions—intimated

[4]In an unpublished piece among the Mark Twain Papers, the first of the "Letters from the Earth," labeled by Paine "Creation of Man," a bolder account of the Creation and of the attributes of God is given. Later Letters in this series grow far more audacious in their handling of the Deity.

xviii

by the continuation "and Hell" which Mark wrote beside the title heading one version of his narrative. "I have tried, all these years," he admitted in his letter to Orion in 1878, "to think of some way of 'doing' hell too—and have always had to give it up. Hell, in my book, will not occupy five pages of MS I judge —it will be only covert hints, I suppose, and quickly dropped; I may end by not even referring to it."[5]

As the tale now stands, the only substantial allusions to hell consist of the Captain's early certitude that he is bound for that port. But this thematic counterpoint tempted Mark repeatedly, as shown for instance by two entries in his notebook for the year 1883:

Stormfield must hear of the man who worked hard all his life to acquire heaven and when he got there the first person he met was a man he had been hoping all the time was in hell—so disappointed and outraged that he inquired the way to hell and took up his satchel and left.

Captain Stormfield finds that hell was originally instituted in deference to an early Christian sentiment. In modern times the halls of heaven are warmed by radiators connected with hell, and the idea is greatly applauded by Jonathan Edwards, Calvin, Baxter & Co. because it adds a new pang to the sinner's suffering to know that the very fire which tortures him is the means of making the righteous comfortable.[6]

[5]This letter from Samuel to Orion Clemens will be found in *Mark Twain's Letters*, ed. Paine (Harper & Brothers, 1917), I, 323.

[6]*Mark Twain's Notebook*, ed. Paine (Harper & Brothers, 1935), 168. Among many entries in the original notebooks which Paine passed over is this notation of November 4, 1893: "Si Wheeler's arrival in Heaven." Garrulous old Simon Wheeler is narrator of "The Celebrated Jumping Frog" story, also hero of one of Mark Twain's stillborn efforts at playwriting, "Simon Wheeler, the Amateur Detective." Was he momentarily intended to supplant Captain Stormfield, or merely supply a diversion?

From his mother—who always warmed the water before she drowned the kittens, and grieved to think of even Satan's damnation—Sam Clemens inherited a tender heart, and the spectacle of sinners in the hands of an angry God never failed to enrage him. The doctrine of eternal punishment he found grotesque and incredible, another proof that vindictive Man had created God in his own ugly image. Hell as seen through Captain Stormfield's eyes doubtless would have developed some sharp sardonic purpose, but the idea never sprouted.

Mark Twain's biographer Paine states that for many years *Captain Stormfield* "lay under the ban" evidently of Mrs. Clemens, in a limbo of projects neither completed nor abandoned. He infers that the tale troubled her lingering sense of churchly decorum, even though Livy herself under Mark's influence through the years grew steadily more broadminded.[7] It is not necessary to go all the way with Van Wyck Brooks in *The Ordeal of Mark Twain,* to grant Mark's deference to her judgment in such matters. Her scruples helped demote "The New Pilgrim's Progress" from title to subtitle of the book that became *The Innocents Abroad,* from fear of seeming to mock a pious classic; caused the deletion from later issues of *Life on the Mississippi* of a plate showing Mark Twain in flames; and prevented publication of his pedestrian gospel of determinism, *What Is Man?,* until Mark himself grew convinced it was a "wicked book" but finally consented to private printing after her death. Livy was extraordinarily sensitive to the "harm" that unconventionality might work, either in causing churchgoers to bridle or else by sapping

[7]Thus in 1879 she admitted to Susan Crane, her adopted sister, that she had ceased to believe in a personal God. Paine's biography, 650-651.

their feeble faith. Such timidity is as hard to imagine today as is the kindred atmosphere of Victorian prudery, but its compulsion was once very real.

And so the celestial adventures of the Captain gathered dust for many a year. Having heard the yarn in 1868, written up a portion soon afterwards and attempted a revision around 1873, Mark kept tinkering with it at intervals. In his journal for March 20, 1878, he sketched a continuation which includes the story as we know it, and a bit beyond:

Have all sorts of heavens—have a gate for each sort.

One gate where they receive a barkeeper with artillery salutes, swarms of angels in the sky and a noble torchlight procession. *He* thinks he is *the* lion of Heaven. Procession over, he drops at once into awful obscurity. But the roughest part of it is that he has to do 3 weeks penance—day and night he must carry a torch and shout himself hoarse, to do honor to some poor scrub whom he wishes had gone to hell.

Wakeman visits these various heavens.

W. is years and years in darkness *between* solar systems.[8]

About eight years later he told his little daughter Susy (as recorded in her precocious biography of him) that "the only book that he had been pertickularly anxious to write was one locked in the safe downstairs, not yet published." Upon

[8]Most of this entry is printed by Paine, *Notebook*, 130, although he cannot resist correcting "whom" to "who." Clemens quotes this entry, grammatical error and all, in a letter to Howells from Heidelberg, June 27, 1878, but carelessly alters "3 weeks" to "30 weeks"—with the remark that in browsing through his notebook "Mrs. Clemens . . . was rather startled to run across this paragraph . . . last night." *The Portable Mark Twain*, ed. Bernard DeVoto (Viking Press, 1946), 754; see also pages 764-765 for another comment on the unfinished tale, to Jeannette Gilder in 1887.

reading Susy's notes again in the mid-1900's Mark Twain commented:

The reference here is to a MS. entitled "Captain Stormfield's Visit to Heaven." It is still in that safe; at least it was still there ten years ago when I saw it last ... I have often thought of finishing it, but was probably beguiled from my half-purpose by some new and sharper interest. I am still intending to finish it, and shall probably continue in that mind indefinitely; it is one of the stabilities of my character that I am always intending to do things.[9]

In dictating his recollections of this story on August 29, 1906, Mark expressed the whim of putting it into his autobiography for publication a half-century hence, "and at that time I shall have been so long under the sod that I shan't care about the results!" Then with a touch of drama he scribbled a postscript. "*Three hours later*. I have just burned the closing two-thirds of it." Constitutionally unable to burn anything he wrote, Mark Twain was here indulging in pure make-believe. He did not burn the manuscript or any part of it, so far as the evidence points. Instead he lifted a portion from the middle, labeled it "Extract from Captain Stormfield's Visit to Heaven," and published it in *Harper's Magazine* in December 1907 and January 1908 prior to its appearance as a slender volume in 1909.

Other parts of the Stormfield story are preserved among his papers, some of them too scrappy or uninspired to be worth salvage. But two opening chapters, marked by Paine

[9] Susy's words are quoted in Paine's biography, 840. Her father's comment is on a detached sheet among his unpublished papers; undated, it refers to the story as "written thirty-three or thirty-four years ago." His dictation of August 29, 1906 concerning the story, cited below, is from *Mark Twain in Eruption*, 248.

"About 1900. A later beginning. Not used," now appear for the first time. Mark Twain's prefatory note tells a little more about his hero. Then follows Captain Stormfield's account of his own death and launching into infinity, and the encounter with his first fellow traveler, Solomon Goldstein. The Mark Twain who once observed, "Jews are members of the human race. Worse than that I cannot say of them," leaves no doubt of his attitude upon a common question of prejudice. The sorrow of this East Side Jew—when Stormfield convinces him that they are both speeding toward hell—that he will never again see his little daughter lately dead, "his playfellow, the apple of his eye," cries out with a special poignancy. One can readily guess that this was written after Clemens's loss in 1896 of his favorite child Susy, a loss made more desolating because the father held no hopes beyond the grave. The next chapter of their flight introduces an Oshkosh citizen suffering from the pangs of dispriz'd love, who has killed himself after assurance that the local Republican majority stands unimpaired. And they meet the Negro named Sam, who gives the Captain a pipe and tobacco, and much friendly solicitude, until Stormfield is led to remark: "He was a good chap, and like his race: I have seen but few niggers that hadn't their hearts in the right place." Here recognizably is the Clemens whose partisanship of the Negro was always so marked that his wife once suggested to him as a mollifying rule, "Consider every man colored until he is proved white." Mark's Paradise, with its red Indians, Chinese, and Arabs—not to mention sky-blue men with seven heads, from other universes—was no preserve of race prejudice.

From these chapters we move readily into the only segment which Mark Twain ever got around to publishing, starting with Stormfield's race against the comét. It suggests the reckless river-packéts in Clemens's pilot days, and also reflécts the personal interest in cométs taken by a man who was born under Halley's in 1835 and believed (quite correctly) that he would die at its next appearance in 1910. The sequence which follows—admission at a wrong gate of Paradise, the magic carpét and arrival at the right address, the choir on the cloud bank, the meeting with a knowledgeable angel named Sandy McWilliams and his description of heavenly days and ways, and reception of the converted barkeeper—fits well enough into the earlier fragment, with only minor inconsistency. Thus the Captain is shepherding a convoy of souls at the close of Chapter II, but at the beginning of the next chapter is hurtling through interstellar space alone. Also, early in the story our hero introduces himself as "Captain Ben Stormfield, late of Fairhaven and 'Frisco" —Fairhaven by way of compliment to Mark's latter-day friend and patron Henry H. Rogers, Standard Oil magnate, who hailed from there—but later the Piute announces him in heaven as "Cap'n Eli Stormfield, of San Francisco."

The torchlight procession welcoming the barkeeper, with which the Stormfield fragment closes, was an honor also promised Andrew Langdon, in the short separate piece now called "Létter from the Recording Angel." This manuscript in the Mark Twain Papers was first published by Bernard DeVoto in *Harper's Magazine*, February 1946. The Recording Angel's balance sheet is rendered supposedly at the close of the year 1887; as DeVoto observes, entries in Mark Twain's

xxiv

notebook for the latter part of that year indicate surprise at the fat profits currently being made by Jervis Langdon & Company, the coal-mining and selling enterprise begun by Mrs. Clemens's late father, whom Mark Twain had deeply admired.[10] But her uncle Andrew, head of the lucrative Buffalo office, is the butt of Mark Twain's savage irony. "Affectionately called Andrew" in heaven, he is hailed as "the meanest white man that ever lived on the face of the earth." Mark Twain inclined to a dim view of most contemporary plutocrats save Henry H. Rogers—witness his comments upon Jay Gould, William A. Clark, Andrew Carnegie, and somewhat more variably the Rockefellers, expressed in *Mark Twain in Eruption*—but his opinion of Andrew Langdon, at least in this mood, was transcendent. Clemens seems briefly to have toyed with the idea of interpolating it into *The Connecticut Yankee;* at least putting his sentiments on paper must have afforded him a purgative satisfaction. It is hard to imagine that this squib had any better chance of passing his domestic censor than the camel through the needle's eye.

Dixon Wecter

Late Literary Executor of
the Mark Twain Estate

[10]One entry reads: "JL & Co's Notes, made to Mrs. C: $17,750; 8,000; 25,000; 2,410. [$53,160.]" Another runs: "JL & Co have been paying out money in the new colliery right along for 3½ years now (Aug. '87) and will continue to do it 3 or 4 more." An accounting to Mrs. Langdon from her brother Charles, dated September 3, 1873, shows that her interest in the Langdon coal company comprised $80,000 out of her estate of roughly a quarter of a million dollars.

Part One ✢ Captain Stormfield's Visit to Heaven

Note. I knew Captain Stormfield well. I made three long sea-voyages with him in his ship. He was a rugged, weather-tanned sailor, with a picked-up education, a sterling good heart, an iron will, abundant pluck, unshakable beliefs and convictions, and a confidence in himself which had no discoverable limits. He was open, frank, communicative, affectionate, and as honest, simple and genuine as a dog. He was deeply religious, by nature and by the training of his mother, and a fluent and desolating swearer by the training of his father and by the necessities of his occupation. He was born in his father's ship,[1] he had spent his entire life at sea, and had seen the edges of all lands and the interiors of none, and when I first knew him he was sixty-five years old and his glossy black hair and whiskers were beginning to show threads of gray; but there was no trace of age in his body, yet, nor in his determined spirit, and the

[1]Several phrases in this first paragraph,—including the statement that the Captain "was born in his father's ship"—are borrowed from the description of Hurricane Jones in "Some Rambling Notes on an Idle Excursion." That statement incidentally is fictitious; Wakeman's memoir shows that by origin he was a Connecticut country boy, and went to sea at the age of fourteen.

fires that burned in his eyes were the fires of youth. He was a lovable man when people pleased him, but a tough person to deal with when the case was otherwise.

He had a good deal of imagination, and it probably colored his statements of fact; but if this was so, he was not aware of it. He made no statement which he did not believe to be true. When he told me about his strange and uncanny adventures in the Devil's Race-Track—a vast area in the solitudes of the South Pacific where the needle of the compass is powerless to exercise its office and whizzes madly and continuously around—I spared him the hurt of suggesting that he had dreamed the tale, for I saw that he was in earnest; but in secret I believed it was only a vision, a dream. Privately I think his visit to the Other World was a dream, also, but I did not wound him with the expression of the thought. He believed that the visit was an actual experience; I accepted it on those terms, listened to it attentively, took down the details of each day's revelations in short-hand, by his permission, then afterward reduced the result to long-hand. I have polished some of the ruggedness out of his grammar and construction, and in places I have cooled off his language a little; otherwise his tale stands here as he told it.

MARK TWAIN

Chapter One

I WAS DYING, AND KNEW IT. I WAS MAKING GASPS, WITH LONG SPACES BETWEEN, AND THEY WERE STANDING AROUND THE BED, QUIET AND STILL, WAITING FOR ME TO GO. Now and then they spoke; and what they said got dimmer and dimmer, and further and further away. I heard it all, though. The mate said—

"He's going out with the tide."

Chips the carpenter said—

"How do you know? No tide out here in the middle of the ocean."

"Yes there is. And anyway, they always do."

It was still again, a while—only the heaving and creaking, and the dull lanterns swinging this way and that, and the wind wheezing and piping, far off. Then I heard a voice, away off—

"Eight bells, sir."

"Make it so," said the mate.

"Ay-ay, sir."

Another voice—

"Freshening up, sir—coming on to blow."

"Sheet home," says the mate. "Reef tops'ls and sky-scrapers, and stand by."

"Ay-ay, sir."

By and by the mate says—

"How's it now?"

"He's cold, up to his ribs," says the doctor. "Give him

ten minutes."

"Everything ready, Chips?"

"Canvas, cannon balls and all, sir."

"Bible and burial service?"

"All handy, sir."

Quiet again, for a while—wind so vague it sounded like dream-wind. Then the doctor's voice—

"Is he prepared for the change, do you think?"

"To hell? Oh, I guess so."

"I reckon there ain't any doubt."

It was Chips said it; kind of mournful, too.

"Doubt?" said the mate. "Hadn't any himself, if that's any sign."

"No," says Chips, "he always said he judged he was booked for there."

Long, long stillness. Then the doctor's voice, so far off and dim it sounded like it was down a deep well—

"There—it's over! Just at 12:14!"

Dark? Oh, pitch dark—all in a second! I was dead, and knew it.

I felt myself make a plunge, and recognized that I was flashing through the air like a bird. I had a quick, dim glimpse of the sea and the ship, then everything was black darkness, and nothing visible, and I went whizzing through it. I said to myself, "I'm all here, clothes and all, nothing missing; they'll sink a counterfeit in the sea; it's not me, I'm all here."

Next, it began to get light, and straight off I plunged into a whole universe of blinding fire, and straight through it. It was 12:22 by my watch.

4

Do you know where I was? In the sun. That was my guess, and it turned out afterwards that I was right. Eight minutes out from port. It gave me my gait—exactly the speed of light, 186,000 miles a second. Ninety-three million miles in eight minutes by the watch. There wasn't ever a prouder ghost. I was as pleased as a child, and wished I had something to race with.

Before I was done thinking these things I was out on the other side and the sun shriveling up to a luminous wad behind me. It was less than a million miles in diameter, and I was through before I had time to get warm. I was in the dark again, now. In the dark; but I myself wasn't dark. My body gave out a soft and ghostly glow and I felt like a lightning bug. I couldn't make out the why of this, but I could read my watch by it, and that was more to the point.

Presently I noticed a glow like my own a little way off, and was glad, and made a trumpet of my hands and hailed it—

"Shipmate ahoy!"

"Same to you!"

"Where from?"

"Chatham Street."

"Whither bound?"

"I vish I knew—aind it?"

"I reckon you're going my way. Name?"

"Solomon Goldstein. Yours?"

"Captain Ben Stormfield, late of Fairhaven and 'Frisco. Come alongside, friend."

He did it. It was a great improvement, having company. I was born sociable, and never could stand solitude. I was

7

trained to a prejudice against Jews—Christians always are, you know—but such of it as I had was in my head, there wasn't any in my heart. But if I had been full of it it would have disappeared then, I was so lonesome and so anxious for company. Dear me, when you are going to—to—where I was going—you are humble-mindeder than you used to be, and thankful for whatever you can get, never mind the quality of it.

We spun along together, and talked, and got acquainted and had a good time. I thought it would be a kindness to Solomon to dissipate his doubts, so that he would have a quiet mind. I could never be comfortable in a state of doubt myself. So I reasoned the thing out, and showed him that his being pointed the same as me was proof of where he was bound for. It cost him a good deal of distress, but in the end he was reconciled and said it was probably best the way it was, he wouldn't be suitable company for angels and they would turn him down if he tried to work in; he had been treated like that in New York, and he judged that the ways of high society were about the same everywhere. He wanted me not to desert him when we got to where we were going, but stay by him, for he would be a stranger and friendless. Poor fellow, I was touched; and promised—"to all eternity."

Then we were quiet a long time, and I let him alone, and let him think. It would do him good. Now and then he sighed, and by and by I found he was crying. You know, I was mad with him in a minute; and says to myself, "Just like a Jew! he has promised some hayseed or other a coat for four dollars, and now he has made up his mind that if he was back he could work off a worse one on him for five. They haven't

8

any heart—that race—nor any principles."

He sobbed along to himself, and I got colder and colder and harder and harder towards him. At last I broke out and said—

"Cheese it! Damn the coat! Drop it out of your mind."

"Goat?"

"Yes. Find something else to cry about."

"Why, I wasn't crying apoud a goat."

"What then?"

"Oh, captain, I loss my little taughter, and now I never, never see her again any more. It break my heart!"

By God, it went through me like a knife! I wouldn't feel so mean again, and so grieved, not for a fleet of ships. And I spoke out and said what I felt; and went on damning myself for a hound till he was so distressed I had to stop; but I wasn't half through. He begged me not to talk so, and said I oughtn't to make so much of what I had done; he said it was only a mistake, and a mistake wasn't a crime.

There now—wasn't it magnanimous? I ask you—wasn't it? I think so. To my mind there was the stuff in him for a Christian; and I came out flat-footed and told him so. And if it hadn't been too late I would have reformed him and made him one, or died in the act.

We were good friends again, and he didn't need to keep his sorrows to himself any more, he could pour them right into my heart, which was wide open and ready; and he did; till it seemed to me I couldn't bear it. Lord, the misery of it! She was his pet, his playfellow, the apple of his eye; she was ten years old, and dead six months, and he was glad to die, himself, so he could have her in his arms again and be with

9

her always—and now that dream was over. Why, she was gone—*forever*. The word had a new meaning. It took my breath, it made me gasp. All our lives we believe we are going to see our lost friends again—we are not disturbed with doubts, we think we *know* it. It is what keeps us alive. And here, in this father's heart that hope was dead. I had never seen that before. This was the first time, and I—why it was I that had killed it. If I had only thought! If I had only kept still, and left him to find it out for himself. He let his tears run, and now and then his trouble wrung a groan out of him, and his lips quivered and he said—

"Poor little Minnie—and poor me."

And to myself I said the same—

"Poor little Minnie—and poor me."

That feeling stayed by me, and never left me. And many's the time, when I was thinking of that poor Jew's disaster, I have said in my thoughts, "I wish I was bound for heaven, and could trade places with him, so he could see his child, damned if I wouldn't do it." If ever you are situated like that, you will understand the feeling.

Chapter Two

WE TALKED LATE, AND FELL ASLEEP PRETTY TIRED, ABOUT TWO IN THE MORNING; HAD A SOUND SLEEP, AND woke refreshed and fine towards noon. Pitch dark, still. We were not hungry, but I could have smoked with a relish, if I had had the things. Also, I could have enjoyed a drink.

We had to stop and think a minute, when we woke, before we came fully to ourselves and realized our situation, for we thought we had been dreaming. In fact it was hard to get rid of the idea that it was all a dream. But we had to get rid of it, and we did. Then a ghastly cold shock went through us—we remembered where we were pointed for. Next, we were astonished. Astonished because we hadn't arrived. Astonished and glad. Glad we hadn't arrived. Hopeful that we might not arrive for some little time yet.

"How far is it that ve haf come, Captain Sthormfilt?"

"Eleven or twelve hundred million miles."

"Ach Gott, it is a speed!"

"Right you are. There isn't anything that can pass us but thought. It would take the lightning express twenty-four or twenty-five days to fly around the globe; we could do it four times in a second—yes, sir, and do it easy. Solomon, I wish we had something to race with."

Along in the afternoon we saw a soft blur of light a little way off, north-east-by-east-half-east, about two points off the weather bow, and hailed it. It closed up on us, and turned out to be a corpse by the name of Bailey, from Oshkosh,

11

that had died at 7:10 the night before. A good creature, but moony and reflective. Republican in politics, and had the idea that nothing could save civilization but that party. He was melancholy, and we got him to talk, so as to cheer him up; and along by spells, as he got to feeling better, his private matters got to leaking out—among others, the fact that he had committed suicide. You know, we had suspected it; he had a hole through his forehead that you couldn't have plugged with a marlinespike.

By and by his spirits sagged again. Then the cause came out. He was delicate and sensitive in his morals, and he had been doing something in politics, the last thing, which he was wondering if it was exactly straight. There was an election to fill a vacancy in his town government, and it was such a close fit that one vote would decide it. He wasn't going to be there to vote—he was going to be up here, with us. But if he could keep a democrat from voting, that would answer just as well, and the republican candidate would pull through. So, when he was ready for suicide he went to a rigidly honorable friend, who was a democrat, and got him to pair off with him. The republican ticket was safe, then, and he killed himself. So he was a little troubled about it, and uncertain; afraid that maybe he hadn't played quite fair, for a Presbyterian.

But Solomon admired him, and thought it was an amazingly smart idea, and just gloated over him with envy, and grinned that Jew grin of intense satisfaction, you know, and slapped his thigh and said—

"Py Chorge, Pailey, almost thou persuadest me to pe a Ghristian."

12

It was about his girl that he killed himself — Candace Miller. He couldn't ever quite get her to say she loved him, though she seemed to, and he had good hopes. But the thing that decided him was a note from her, in which she told him she loved him as a friend, and hoped they would always be friends, but she found her heart belonged to another. Poor Bailey, he broke down there and cried.

Curious! Just then we sighted a blue light a little astern, and hailed it, and when it ranged up alongside Bailey shouted—

"Why Tom Wilson! what a happy surprise; what ever brought you here, comrade?"

Wilson gave him an appealing look that was sort of heartbreaking to see, and said—

"Don't welcome me like that, George, I'm not worthy. I'm a low-down dog, and not fit for any clean man's company."

"Don't!" said Bailey. "Don't talk like that. What is it?"

"George, I did a treacherous thing. To think I could do it to an old playfellow like you, that I was born and raised with! But it was only a silly practical joke, and I never dreamed that any harm could come of it. I wrote that letter. She loved you, George."

"My God!"

"Yes, she did. She was the first one to the house; and when she saw you lying dead in your blood and the letter by you, signed with her name, she read it and knew! She flung herself on your corpse, and kissed your face and your eyes, and poured out her love and her grief and despair, and I saw it. I had murdered you, I had broken her heart,

13

I couldn't bear it—and I am here."

Another suicide, you see. Bailey—well, he couldn't go back, you know, and it was pitiful to see him, he was so frantic over what he had lost by killing himself before ever stopping to find out whether she wrote the letter or not. He kept on regretting and lamenting and wishing he had waited and been more rational, and arranging over and over again in different ways, how he ought to have acted, and how he would act now, if he could only have the chance over again. All no good, of course, and made us miserable to hear it, for he couldn't ever have his chance again forever—we realized that, and the whole ghastliness of the situation. Some people think you are at rest when you die. Let them wait, they'll see.

Solomon took Bailey aside to comfort him—a good idea; people that carry griefs in their hearts know how to comfort others' griefs.

We whizzed along about a week before we picked up another straggler. This time it was a nigger. He was about thirty-eight or forty, and had been a slave nearly half of his life. Named Sam. A cheerful, good-natured cuss, and likable. As I learned later, a pick-up is a depressing influence upon the company for some time, because he is full of thinkings about his people at home and their grief over losing him; and so his talk is all about that, and he wants sympathy, and cries a good deal, and tells you how dear and good his wife was, or his poor old mother, or his sisters and brothers, and of course in common kindness you have to listen, and it keeps the company feeling desolate and wretched for days together, and starts up their own sorrows over their own loss of fam-

14

ily and friends; but when the pick-up is a young person that has lost a sweetheart, that is the worst. There isn't any end to their talk, and their sorrow and their tears. And dear, dear, that one tiresome everlasting question that they keep on asking till you are worn to the bone with it: *don't* we think he (or she) will die soon, and come? What can you say? There's only one thing: *yes*, we hope he will. And when you have said it a couple of thousand times, you lose patience and wish you hadn't died. But dead people are people, just the same, and they bring their habits with them, which is natural. On the earth, when you arrive in a city—any city on the globe—the people peck at you with the same old regular questions—

"First time you have visited our city?"

"How does it impress you?"

"When did you arrive?"

"How long are you going to stay?"

Sometimes you have to leave next day, to get a rest. We arranged differently with the lovers, by and by: we bunched them together to themselves and made them burn their own smoke. And it was no harm; they like it best that way. There was plenty of sympathy and sentiment, and that was what they wanted.

Sam had pipe, tobacco and matches; I cannot tell you how glad I was. But only for a little moment; then there was a sharp disappointment: the matches wouldn't light. Bailey explained it: there was no atmosphere there in space, and the match couldn't burn without oxygen. I said we would keep the things—we might strike through the atmosphere of a planet or a sun, some time or other, and if it was a big

15

one we might have time for one whiff, anyway. But he said no, it wasn't on the cards.

"Ours are spiritualized bodies and spiritualized clothes and things," he said, "otherwise they would have been consumed in a flash when we first darted through the earth's atmosphere. This is spiritualized tobacco, and fire-proof."

It was very annoying. But I said we would keep it, just the same—

"It will burn in hell, anyway."

When the nigger found that that was where I was going, it filled him with distress, and he hoped I was mistaken, and did his best to persuade me I was; but I hadn't any doubts, and so he had to give in. He was as grieved about it as my best friend could be, and tried his best to believe it wouldn't be as hot there as people said, and hoped and believed I would get used to it after a while, and not mind it. His kindly talk won me completely; and when he gave me the pipe and tobacco, and begged me to think of him sometimes when I was smoking, I was a good deal moved. He was a good chap, and like his race: I have seen but few niggers that hadn't their hearts in the right place.

As week after week slipped along by we picked up a straggler at intervals, and at the end of the first year our herd numbered 36. It looked like a flock of glow-worms, and was a quite pretty sight. We could have had a regiment if we had kept all we came across, but the speeds were various and that was an interference. The slowest ship makes the pace for the fleet, of course. I raised our gait a little, as an accommodation, and established it at 200,000 miles a second. Some wanted to get on faster, on account of wanting to join

16

lost friends, so we let them go. I was not in a particular hurry, myself—my business would keep. Some that had been consumptives and such like, were rickety and slow, and they dropped behind and disappeared. Some that were troublesome and disagreeable, and always raising Cain over any little thing that didn't suit them, I ordered off the course, with a competent cursing and a warning to stand clear. We had all sorts left, young and old, and on the whole they were satisfactory enough, though a few of them were not up to standard, I will admit.

Chapter Three

WELL, WHEN I HAD BEEN DEAD ABOUT THIRTY YEARS, I BEGUN TO GET A LITTLE ANXIOUS. MIND YOU, I HAD BEEN whizzing through space all that time, like a comet. *Like* a comet! Why, Peters, I laid over the lot of them! Of course there warn't any of them going my way, as a steady thing, you know, because they travel in a long circle like the loop of a lasso, whereas I was pointed as straight as a dart for the Hereafter; but I happened on one every now and then that was going my way for an hour or so, and then we had a bit of a brush together. But it was generally pretty one-sided, because I sailed by them the same as if they were standing still. An ordinary comet don't make more than about 200,000 miles a minute. Of course when I came across one of that sort—like Encke's and Halley's comets, for instance—it warn't anything but just a flash and a vanish, you see. You couldn't rightly call it a race. It was as if the comet was a gravel-train and I was a telegraph despatch. But after I got outside of our astronomical system, I used to flush a comet occasionally that was something *like*. *We* haven't got any such comets—ours don't begin. One night I was swinging along at a good round gait, everything taut and trim, and the wind in my favor—I judged I was going about a million miles a minute—it might have been more, it couldn't have been less—when I flushed a most uncommonly big one about three points off my starboard bow. By his stern lights I judged he was bearing about northeast-and-by-north-half-east. Well, it was so near my course that I wouldn't throw away the chance; so I fell off a point, steadied my helm, and went for him. You should have heard me whiz, and seen the electric fur fly! In about a minute and a half I was fringed out with an electrical nimbus that flamed around for miles and miles and lit up all space like broad day. The comet was burning blue in the distance, like a sickly torch, when I first sighted him, but he begun to grow bigger and bigger as I crept up on him. I slipped up on him so fast that when I had gone about 150,000,000 miles I was close enough to be swallowed up in the phosphorescent glory of his wake, and I couldn't see anything for the glare. Thinks I, it won't do to run into him, so I shunted to one side and tore along. By and by I closed up abreast of his tail. Do you know what it was like? It was like a gnat closing up on the continent of America. I forged along. By and by I had sailed along his coast for a little upwards of a hundred and fifty million miles, and then I could see by the shape of him that I hadn't even got up to his waistband yet. Why, Peters, *we* don't know anything about comets, down here. If you want to see comets that *are* comets, you've got to go outside of our solar system — where there's room for them, you understand. My friend, I've seen comets out there that couldn't even lay down inside the *orbits* of our noblest comets without their tails hanging over.

Well, I boomed along another hundred and fifty million miles, and got up abreast his shoulder, as you may say. I was feeling pretty fine, I tell you; but just then I noticed the officer of the deck come to the side and hoist his glass in my direction. Straight off I heard him sing out—

19

"Below there, ahoy! Shake her up, shake her up! Heave on a hundred million billion tons of brimstone!"

"Ay—ay, sir!"

"Pipe the stabboard watch! All hands on deck!"

"Ay—ay, sir!"

"Send two hundred thousand million men aloft to shake out royals and sky-scrapers!"

"Ay—ay, sir!"

"Hand the stuns'ls! Hang out every rag you've got! Clothe her from stem to rudder-post!"

"Ay—ay, sir!"

In about a second I begun to see I'd woke up a pretty ugly customer, Peters. In less than ten seconds that comet was just a blazing cloud of red-hot canvas. It was piled up into the heavens clean out of sight—the old thing seemed to swell out and occupy all space; the sulphur smoke from the furnaces—oh, well, nobody can describe the way it rolled and tumbled up into the skies, and nobody can half describe the way it smelt. Neither can anybody begin to describe the way that monstrous craft begun to crash along. And such another powpow—thousands of bo's'n's whistles screaming at once, and a crew like the populations of a hundred thousand worlds like ours all swearing at once. Well, I never heard the like of it before.

We roared and thundered along side by side, both doing our level best, because I'd never struck a comet before that could lay over me, and so I was bound to beat this one or break something. I judged I had some reputation in space, and I calculated to keep it. I noticed I wasn't gaining as fast, now, as I was before, but still I was gaining. There was a power of excitement on board the comet. Upwards of a hundred billion passengers swarmed up from below and rushed to the side and begun to bet on the race. Of course this careened her and damaged her speed. My, but wasn't the mate mad! He jumped at the crowd, with his trumpet in his hand, and sung out—

"Amidships! amidships, you——![1] or I'll brain the last idiot of you!"

Well, sir, I gained and gained, little by little, till at last I went skimming sweetly by the magnificent old conflagration's nose. By this time the captain of the comet had been rousted out, and he stood there in the red glare for'ard, by the mate, in his shirt-sleeves and slippers, his hair all rats' nests and one suspender hanging, and how sick those two men did look! I just simply couldn't help putting my thumb to my nose as I glided away and singing out:

"Ta-ta! ta-ta! Any word to send to your family?"

Peters, it was a mistake. Yes, sir, I've often regretted that —it was a mistake. You see, the captain had given up the race, but that remark was too tedious for him—he couldn't stand it. He turned to the mate, and says he—

"Have we got brimstone enough of our own to make the trip?"

"Yes, sir."

"Sure?"

"Yes, sir, more than enough."

"How much have we got in cargo for Satan?"

---

[1] The captain could not remember what this word was. He said it was in a foreign tongue.

21

"Eighteen hundred thousand billion quintillions of ka-zarks."

"Very well, then, let his boarders freeze till the next com-et comes. Lighten ship! Lively, now, lively, men! Heave the whole cargo overboard!"

Peters, look me in the eye, and be calm. I found out, over there, that a kazark is exactly the bulk of a *hundred and sixty-nine worlds like ours!* They hove all that load overboard. When it fell it wiped out a considerable raft of stars just as clean as if they'd been candles and somebody blowed them out. As for the race, that was at an end. The minute she was lightened the comet swung along by me the same as if I was anchored. The captain stood on the stern, by the after-davits, and put his thumb to his nose and sung out—

"Ta-ta! ta-ta! Maybe *you've* got some message to send your friends in the Everlasting Tropics!"

Then he hove up his other suspender and started for'ard, and inside of three-quarters of an hour his craft was only a pale torch again in the distance. Yes, it was a mistake, Peters —that remark of mine. I don't reckon I'll ever get over being sorry about it. I'd 'a' beat the bully of the firmament if I'd kept my mouth shut.

But I've wandered a little off the track of my tale; I'll get back on my course again. Now you see what kind of speed I was making. So, as I said, when I had been tearing along this way about thirty years I begun to get uneasy. Oh, it was pleasant enough, with a good deal to find out, but then it was kind of lonesome, you know. Besides, I wanted to get somewhere. I hadn't shipped with the idea of cruising forever. First off, I liked the delay, because I judged I was going to fetch up in pretty warm quarters when I got through; but towards the last I begun to feel that I'd rather go to—well, most any place, so as to finish up the uncertainty.

Well, one night—it was always night, except when I was rushing by some star that was occupying the whole universe with its fire and its glare—light enough then, of course, but I necessarily left it behind in a minute or two and plunged into a solid week of darkness again. The stars ain't so close together as they look to be. Where was I? Oh yes; one night I was sailing along, when I discovered a tremendous long row of blinking lights away on the horizon ahead. As I approached, they begun to tower and swell and look like mighty furnaces. Says I to myself—

"By George, I've arrived at last—and at the wrong place, just as I expected!"

Then I fainted. I don't know how long I was insensible, but it must have been a good while, for, when I came to, the darkness was all gone and there was the loveliest sunshine and the balmiest, fragrantest air in its place. And there was such a marvellous world spread out before me—such a glowing, beautiful, bewitching country. The things I took for furnaces were gates, miles high, made all of flashing jewels, and they pierced a wall of solid gold that you couldn't see the top of, nor yet the end of, in either direction. I was pointed straight for one of these gates, and a-coming like a house afire. Now I noticed that the skies were black with millions of people, pointed for those gates. What a roar they made, rushing through the air! The ground was as thick as ants with people, too—billions of them, I judge.

23

I lit. I drifted up to a gate with a swarm of people, and when it was my turn the head clerk says, in a businesslike way—

"Well, quick! Where are you from?"

"San Francisco," says I.

"San Fran—*what*?" says he.

"San Francisco."

He scratched his head and looked puzzled, then he says—

"Is it a planet?"

By George, Peters, think of it! "*Planet*?" says I; "it's a city. And moreover, it's one of the biggest and finest and—"

"There, there!" says he, "no time here for conversation. We don't deal in cities here. Where are you from in a *general* way?"

"Oh," I says, "I beg your pardon. Put me down for California."

I had him *again*, Peters! He puzzled a second, then he says, sharp and irritable—

"I don't know any such planet—is it a constellation?"

"Oh, my goodness!" says I. "Constellation, says you? No—it's a State."

"Man, we don't deal in States here. *Will* you tell me where you are from *in general*—at large, don't you understand?"

"Oh, now I get your idea," I says. "I'm from America— the United States of America."

Peters, do you know I had him *again*? If I hadn't I'm a clam! His face was as blank as a target after a militia shooting-match. He turned to an under clerk and says—

"Where is America? *What* is America?"

The under clerk answered up prompt and says—

24

"There ain't any such orb."

"Orb?" says I. "Why, what are you talking about, young man? It ain't an orb; it's a country; it's a continent. Columbus discovered it; I reckon likely you've heard of *him*, anyway. America—why, sir, America—

"Silence!" says the head clerk. "Once for all, where—are—you—*from?*"

"Well," says I, "I don't know anything more to say—unless I lump things, and just say I'm from the world."

"Ah," says he, brightening up, "now that's something like! *What* world?"

Peters, he had *me*, that time. I looked at him, puzzled, he looked at me, worried. Then he burst out—

"Come, come, what world?"

Says I, "Why, *the* world, of course."

"*The* world!" he says. "H'm! there's billions of them! ... Next!"

That meant for me to stand aside. I done so, and a sky-blue man with seven heads and only one leg hopped into my place. I took a walk. It just occurred to me, then, that all the myriads I had seen swarming to that gate, up to this time, were just like that creature. I tried to run across somebody I was acquainted with, but they were out of acquaintances of mine just then. So I thought the thing all over and finally sidled back there pretty meek and feeling rather stumped, as you may say.

"Well?" said the head clerk.

"Well, sir," I says, pretty humble, "I don't seem to make out which world it is I'm from. But you may know it from this—it's the one the Saviour saved."

25

He bent his head at the Name. Then he says, gently—

"The worlds He has saved are like to the gates of heaven in number—none can count them. What astronomical system is your world in?—perhaps that may assist."

"It's the one that has the sun in it—and the moon—and Mars"—he shook his head at each name—hadn't ever heard of them, you see—"and Neptune—and Uranus—and Jupiter—"

"Hold on!" says he—"hold on a minute! Jupiter . . . Jupiter . . . Seems to me we had a man from there eight or nine hundred years ago—but people from that system very seldom enter by this gate." All of a sudden he begun to look me so straight in the eye that I thought he was going to bore through me. Then he says, very deliberate, "Did you come *straight here* from your system?"

"Yes, sir," I says—but I blushed the least little bit in the world when I said it.

He looked at me very stern, and says—

"That is not true; and this is not the place for prevarication. You wandered from your course. How did that happen?"

Says I, blushing again—

"I'm sorry, and I take back what I said, and confess. I raced a little with a comet one day—only just the least little bit—only the tiniest lit—"

"So—so," says he—and without any sugar in his voice to speak of.

I went on, and says—

"But I only fell off just a bare point, and I went right back on my course again the minute the race was over."

26

"No matter—that divergence has made all this trouble. It has brought you to a gate that is billions of leagues from the right one. If you had gone to your own gate they would have known all about your world at once and there would have been no delay. But we will try to accommodate you." He turned to an under clerk and says—

"What system is Jupiter in?"

"I don't remember, sir, but I think there is such a planet in one of the little new systems away out in one of the thinly worlded corners of the universe. I will see."

He got a balloon and sailed up and up and up, in front of a map that was as big as Rhode Island. He went on till he was out of sight, and by and by he came down and got something to eat and went up again. To cut a long story short, he kept on doing this for a day or two, and finally he came down and said he thought he had found that solar system, but it might be fly-specks. So he got a microscope and went back. It turned out better than he feared. He had rousted out our system, sure enough. He got me to describe our planet and its distance from the sun, and then he says to his chief—

"Oh, I know the one he means, now, sir. It is on the map. It is called the Wart."

Says I to myself, "Young man, it wouldn't be wholesome for you to go down *there* and call it the Wart."

Well, they let me in, then, and told me I was safe forever and wouldn't have any more trouble.

Then they turned from me and went on with their work, the same as if they considered my case all complete and ship-shape. I was a good deal surprised at this, but I was diffident

about speaking up and reminding them. I did so hate to do it, you know; it seemed a pity to bother them, they had so much on their hands. Twice I thought I would give up and let the thing go; so twice I started to leave, but immediately I thought what a figure I should cut stepping out amongst the redeemed in such a rig, and that made me hang back and come to anchor again. People got to eying me—clerks, you know—wondering why I didn't get under way. I couldn't stand this long—it was too uncomfortable. So at last I

28

plucked up courage and tipped the head clerk a signal. He says—

"What! you here yet? What's wanting?"

Says I, in a low voice and very confidential, making a trumpet with my hand at his ear—

"I beg pardon, and you mustn't mind my reminding you, and seeming to meddle, but hain't you forgot something?"

He studied a second, and says—

"Forgot something? . . . No, not that I know of."

"Think," says I.

He thought. Then he says—

"No, I can't seem to have forgot anything. What is it?"

"Look at me," says I, "look me all over."

He done it.

"Well?" says he.

"Well," says I, "you don't notice anything? If I branched out amongst the elect looking like this, wouldn't I attract considerable attention?—wouldn't I be a little conspicuous?"

"Well," he says, "I don't see anything the matter. What do you lack?"

"Lack! Why, I lack my harp, and my wreath, and my halo, and my hymn-book, and my palm branch—I lack everything that a body naturally requires up here, my friend."

Puzzled? Peters, he was the worst puzzled man you ever saw. Finally he says—

"Well, you seem to be a curiosity every way a body takes you. I never heard of these things before."

I looked at the man awhile in solid astonishment; then I says—

"Now, I hope you don't take it as an offence, for I don't

29

mean any, but really, for a man that has been in the Kingdom as long as I reckon you have, you do seem to know powerful little about its customs."

"Its customs!" says he. "Heaven is a large place, good friend. Large empires have many and diverse customs. Even small dominions have, as you know by what you have seen of the matter on a small scale in the Wart. How can you imagine I could ever learn the varied customs of the countless kingdoms of heaven? It makes my head ache to think of it. I know the customs that prevail in those portions inhabited by peoples that are appointed to enter by my own gate—and hark ye, that is quite enough knowledge for one individual to try to pack into his head in the thirty-seven millions of years I have devoted night and day to that study. But the idea of learning the customs of the whole appalling expanse of heaven—O man, how insanely you talk! Now I don't doubt that this odd costume you talk about is the fashion in that district of heaven you belong to, but you won't be conspicuous in this section without it."

I felt all right, if that was the case, so I bade him goodday and left. All day I walked towards the far end of a prodigious hall of the office, hoping to come out into heaven any moment, but it was a mistake. That hall was built on the general heavenly plan—it naturally couldn't be small. At last I got so tired I couldn't go any farther; so I sat down to rest, and begun to tackle the queerest sort of strangers and ask for information; but I didn't get any; they couldn't understand my language, and I could not understand theirs. I got dreadfully lonesome. I was so downhearted and homesick I wished a hundred times I never had died. I turned back,

of course. About noon next day, I got back at last and was on hand at the booking-office once more. Says I to the head clerk—

"I begin to see that a man's got to be in his own heaven to be happy."

"Perfectly correct," says he. "Did you imagine the same heaven would suit all sorts of men?"

"Well, I had that idea—but I see the foolishness of it. Which way am I to go to get to my district?"

He called the under clerk that had examined the map, and he gave me general directions. I thanked him and started; but he says—

"Wait a minute; it is millions of leagues from here. Go outside and stand on that red wishing-carpet; shut your eyes, hold your breath, and wish yourself there."

"I'm much obliged," says I; "why didn't you dart me through when I first arrived?"

"We have a good deal to think of here; it was your place to think of it and ask for it. Good-by; we probably shan't see you in this region for a thousand centuries or so."

"In that case, o revoor," says I.

I hopped onto the carpet and held my breath and shut my eyes and wished I was in the booking-office of my own section. The very next instant a voice I knew sung out in a business kind of way—

"A harp and a hymn-book, pair of wings and a halo, size 13, for Cap'n Eli Stormfield, of San Francisco!—make him out a clean bill of health, and let him in."

I opened my eyes. Sure enough, it was a Pi Ute Injun I used to know in Tulare County; mighty good fellow—I remember being at his funeral, which consisted of him being burnt and the other Injuns gauming their faces with his ashes and howling like wildcats. He was powerful glad to see me, and you may make up your mind I was just as glad to see him, and feel that I was in the right kind of a heaven at last.

Just as far as your eye could reach, there was swarms of clerks, running and bustling around, tricking out thousands of Yanks and Mexicans and English and A-rabs, and all sorts of people in their new outfits; and when they gave me my kit and I put on my halo and took a look in the glass, I could have jumped over a house for joy, I was so happy.

"Now *this* is something like!" says I.

"Now," says I, "I'm all right—show me a cloud."

Inside of fifteen minutes I was a mile on my way towards the cloud-banks and about a million people along with me. Most of us tried to fly, but some got crippled and nobody made a success of it. So we concluded to walk, for the present, till we had had some wing practice.

We begun to meet swarms of folks who were coming back. Some had harps and nothing else; some had hymn-books and nothing else; some had nothing at all; all of them looked meek and uncomfortable; one young fellow hadn't anything left but his halo, and he was carrying that in his hand; all of a sudden he offered it to me and says—

"Will you hold it for me a minute?"

Then he disappeared in the crowd. I went on. A woman asked me to hold her palm branch, and then *she* disappeared. A girl got me to hold her harp for her, and by George, *she* disappeared; and so on and so on, till I was about loaded

down to the guards. Then comes a smiling old gentleman and asked me to hold *his* things. I swabbed off the perspiration and says, prétty tart—

"I'll have to gét you to excuse me, my friend,—J ain't no hat-rack."

About this time I begun to run across piles of those traps, lying in the road. I just quiétly dumped my extra cargo along with them. I looked around, and, Peters, that whole nation that was following me were loaded down the same as I'd been. The return crowd had got them to hold their things a minute, you see. They all dumped their loads, too, and we went on.

When I found myself perched on a cloud, with a million other people, I never felt so good in my life. Says I, "Now this is according to the promises; I've been having my doubts, but now I *am* in heaven, sure enough." I gave my palm branch a wave or two, for luck, and then I tautened up my harp-strings and struck in. Well, Peters, you can't imagine anything like the row we made. It was grand to listen to, and made a body thrill all over, but there was considerable many tunes going on at once, and that was a drawback to the harmony, you understand; and then there was a lot of Injun tribes, and they kept up such another war-whooping that they kind of took the tuck out of the music. By and by I quit performing, and judged I'd take a rest. There was quite a nice mild old gentleman sitting next me, and I noticed he didn't take a hand; I encouraged him, but he said he was naturally bashful, and was afraid to try before so many people. By and by the old gentleman said he never could seem to enjoy music somehow. The faćt was I was beginning to

37

feel the same way; but I didn't say anything. Him and I had a considerable long silence, then, but of course it warn't noticeable in that place. After about sixteen or seventeen hours, during which I played and sung a little, now and then— always the same tune, because I didn't know any other— I laid down my harp and begun to fan myself with my palm branch. Then we both got to sighing pretty regular. Finally, says he—

"Don't you know any tune but the one you've been pegging at all day?"

"Not another blessed one," says I.

"Don't you reckon you could learn another one?" says he.

"Never," says I; "I've tried to, but I couldn't manage it."

"It's a long time to hang to the one—eternity, you know."

"Don't break my heart," says I; "I'm getting low-spirited enough already."

After another long silence, says he—

"Are you glad to be here?"

Says I, "Old man, I'll be frank with you. This *ain't* just as near my idea of bliss as I thought it was going to be, when I used to go to church."

Says he, "What do you say to knocking off and calling it half a day?"

"That's me," says I. "I never wanted to get off watch so bad in my life."

So we started. Millions were coming to the cloud-bank all the time, happy and hosannahing; millions were leaving it all the time, looking mighty quiet, I tell you. We laid for the new-comers, and pretty soon I'd got them to hold my things a minute, and then I was a free man again and most

38

outrageously happy. Just then I ran across old Sam Bartlett, who had been dead a long time, and stopped to have a talk with him. Says I—

"Now tell me— is this to go on forever? Ain't there anything else for a change?"

Says he—

"I'll sét you right on that point very quick. People take the figurative language of the Bible and the allegories for literal, and the first thing they ask for when they gét here is a halo and a harp, and so on. Nothing that's harmless and reasonable is refused a body here, if he asks it in the right spirit. So they are outfitted with these things without a word. They go and sing and play just about one day, and that's the last you'll ever see them in the choir. They don't need anybody to tell them that that sort of thing wouldn't make a heaven— at least not a heaven that a sane man could stand a week and remain sane. That cloud-bank is placed where the noise can't disturb the old inhabitants, and so there ain't any harm in létting everybody gét up there and cure himself as soon as he comes.

"Now you just remember this—heaven is as blissful and lovely as it can be; but it's just the busiest place you ever heard of. There ain't any idle people here after the first day. Singing hymns and waving palm branches through all eternity is prétty when you hear about it in the pulpit, but it's as poor a way to put in valuable time as a body could contrive. It would just make a heaven of warbling ignoramuses, don't you see? Eternal Rest sounds comforting in the pulpit, too. Well, you try it once, and see how heavy time will hang on your hands. Why, Stormfield, a man like you, that had

41

been active and stirring all his life, would go mad in six months in a heaven where he hadn't anything to do. Heaven is the very last place to come to rest in,—and don't you be afraid to bet on that!"

Says I—

"Sam, I'm as glad to hear it as I thought I'd be sorry. I'm glad I come, now."

Says he—

"Cap'n, ain't you pretty physically tired?"

Says I—

"Sam, it ain't any name for it! I'm dog-tired."

"Just so—just so. You've earned a good sleep, and you'll get it. You've earned a good appetite, and you'll enjoy your dinner. It's the same here as it is on earth—you've got to earn a thing, square and honest, before you enjoy it. You can't enjoy first and earn afterwards. But there's this differ- ence, here: you can choose your own occupation, and all the powers of heaven will be put forth to help you make a success of it, if you do your level best. The shoemaker on earth that had the soul of a poet in him won't have to make shoes here."

"Now that's all reasonable and right," says I. "Plenty of work, and the kind you hanker after; no more pain, no more suffering—"

"Oh, hold on; there's plenty of pain here—but it don't kill. There's plenty of suffering here, but it don't last. You see, happiness ain't a *thing in itself*—it's only a *contrast* with something that ain't pleasant. That's all it is. There ain't a thing you can mention that is happiness in its own self— it's only so by contrast with the other thing. And so, as soon

42

as the novelty is over and the force of the contrast dulled, it ain't happiness any longer, and you have to gèt something fresh. Well, there's plenty of pain and suffering in heaven —consequently there's plenty of contrasts and just no end of happiness."

Says I, "It's the sensiblest heaven I've heard of yèt, Sam, though it's about as different from the one I was brought up on as a live princess is different from her own wax figger."

Along in the first months I knocked around about the Kingdom, making friends and finally settled down in a prètty likely region, to have a rest before taking another start. I went on making acquaintances and gathering up information. I had a good deal of talk with an old bald-headed angel by the name of Sandy McWilliams. He was from somewhere in New Jersey. I went about with him, considerable. We used to lay around, warm afternoons, in the shade of a rock, on some meadow-ground that was prètty high and out of the marshy slush of his cranberry-farm, and there we used to talk about all kinds of things and smoke pipes. One day, says I—

"About how old might you be, Sandy?"

"Seventy-two."

"I judged so. How long you been in heaven?"

"Twenty-seven years, come Christmas."

"How old was you when you come up?"

"Why, seventy-two, of course."

"You can't mean it!"

"Why can't I mean it?"

"Because, if you was seventy-two then, you are naturally

ninety-nine now."

"No, but I ain't. I stay the same age I was when I come."

"Well," says I, "come to think, there's something just here that I want to ask about. Down below, I always had an idea that in heaven we would all be young, and bright, and spry."

"Well, you *can* be young if you want to. You've only got to wish."

"Well, then why didn't you wish?"

"I did. They all did. You'll try it, some day, like enough; but you'll get tired of the change pretty soon."

"Why?"

"Well, I'll tell you. Now you've always been a sailor; did you ever try some other business?"

"Yes, I tried keeping grocery, once, up in the mines; but I couldn't stand it; it was too dull—no stir, no storm, no life about it; it was like being part dead and part alive, both at the same time. I wanted to be one thing or t'other. I shut up shop pretty quick and went to sea."

"That's it. Grocery people like it, but you couldn't. You see you wasn't used to it. Well, I wasn't used to being young, and I couldn't seem to take any interest in it. I was strong, and handsome, and had curly hair,—yes, and wings, too!—gay wings like a butterfly. I went to picnics and dances and parties with the fellows, and tried to carry on and talk nonsense with the girls, but it wasn't any use; I couldn't take to it—fact is, it was an awful bore. What I wanted was early to bed and early to rise, and something to *do*; and when my work was done, I wanted to sit quiet, and smoke and think—not tear around with a parcel of

44

giddy young kids. You can't think what I suffered whilst I was young."

"How long was you young?"

"Only two weeks. That was plenty for me. Laws, I was so lonesome! You see, I was full of the knowledge and experience of seventy-two years; the deepest subject those young folks could strike was only *a-b-c* to me. And to hear them argue—oh, my! it would have been funny, if it hadn't been so pitiful. Well, I was so hungry for the ways and the sober talk I was used to, that I tried to ring in with the old people, but they wouldn't have it. They considered me a conceited young upstart, and gave me the cold shoulder. Two weeks was a-plenty for me. I was glad to get back my bald head again, and my pipe, and my old drowsy reflections in the shade of a rock or a tree."

"Well," says I, "do you mean to say you're going to stand still at seventy-two, forever?"

"I don't know, and I ain't particular. But I ain't going to drop back to twenty-five any more—I know that, mighty well. I know a sight more than I did twenty-seven years ago, and I enjoy learning, all the time, but I don't seem to get any older. That is, bodily—my mind gets older, and stronger, and better seasoned, and more satisfactory."

Says I, "If a man comes here at ninety, don't he ever set himself back?"

"Of course he does. He sets himself back to fourteen; tries it a couple of hours, and feels like a fool; sets himself forward to twenty; it ain't much improvement; tries thirty, fifty, eighty, and finally ninety—finds he is more at home and comfortable at the same old figure he is used to than

47

any other way. Or, if his mind begun to fail him on earth at eighty, that's where he finally sticks up here. He sticks at the place where his mind was last at its best, for there's where his enjoyment is best, and his ways most set and established."

"Does a chap of twenty-five stay always twenty-five, and look it?"

"If he is a fool, yes. But if he is bright, and ambitious and industrious, the knowledge he gains and the experiences he has, change his ways and thoughts and likings, and make him find his best pleasure in the company of people above that age; so he allows his body to take on that look of as many added years as he needs to make him comfortable and proper in that sort of society; he lets his body go on taking the look of age, according as he progresses, and by and by he will be bald and wrinkled outside, and wise and deep within."

"Babies the same?"

"Babies the same. Laws, what asses we used to be, on earth, about these things! We said we'd be always young in heaven. We didn't say *how* young—we didn't think of that, perhaps—that is, we didn't all think alike, anyway. When I was a boy of seven, I suppose I thought we'd all be twelve, in heaven; when I was twelve, I suppose I thought we'd all be eighteen or twenty in heaven; when I was forty, I begun to go back; I remember I hoped we'd all be about *thirty* years old in heaven. Neither a man nor a boy ever thinks the age he *has* is exactly the best one—he puts the *right* age a few years older or a few years younger than he is. Then he makes that ideal age the general age of the heavenly

48

people. And he expects everybody *to* *stick* at that age—stand stock-still—and expects them to enjoy it!—Now just think of the idea of standing still in heaven! Think of a heaven made up entirely of hoop-rolling, marble-playing cubs of seven years!—or of awkward, diffident, sentimental im- maturities of nineteen—or of vigorous people of thirty, healthy-minded, brimming with ambition, but chained hand and foot to that one age and its limitations like so many galley-slaves! Think of the dull sameness of a society made up of people all of one age and one set of looks, habits, tastes and feelings. Think how superior to it earth would be, with its variety of types and faces and ages, and the enlivening attrition of the myriad interests that come into pleasant collision in such a variegated society."

"Look here," says I, "do you know what you're doing?"

"Well, what am I doing?"

"You are making heaven pretty comfortable in one way, but you are playing the mischief with it in another."

"How d'you mean?"

"Well," I says, "take a young mother that's lost her child, and—"

"'Sh!" he says. "Look!"

It was a woman. Middle-aged, and had grizzled hair. She was walking slow, and her head was bent down, and her wings hanging limp and droopy; and she looked ever so tired, and was crying, poor thing! She passed along by, with her head down, that way, and the tears running down her face, and didn't see us. Then Sandy said, low and gentle, and full of pity:

"*She's* hunting for her child! No, *found* it, I reckon. Lord,

49

how she's changed! But I recognized her in a minute, though it's twenty-seven years since I saw her. A young mother she was, about twenty-two or four, or along there; and blooming and lovely and sweet? oh, just a flower! And all her heart and all her soul was wrapped up in her child, her little girl, two years old. And it died, and she went wild with grief, just wild! Well, the only comfort she had was that she'd see her child again, in heaven— 'never more to part,' she said, and kept on saying it over and over, 'never more to part.' And the words made her happy; yes, they did; they made her joyful; and when I was dying, twenty-seven years ago, she told me to find her child the first thing, and say she was coming— 'soon, soon, *very* soon, she hoped and believed!' "

"Why, it's pitiful, Sandy."

He didn't say anything for a while, but sat looking at the ground, thinking. Then he says, kind of mournful:

"And now she's come!"

"Well? Go on."

"Stormfield, maybe she hasn't found the child, but J think she has. Looks so to me. I've seen cases before. You see, she's kept that child in her head just the same as it was when she jounced it in her arms a little chubby thing. But here it didn't elect to *stay* a child. No, it elected to grow up, which it did. And in these twenty-seven years it has learned all the deep scientific learning there is to learn, and is studying and studying and learning and learning more and more, all the time, and don't give a damn for anything *but* learning; just learning, and discussing gigantic problems with people like herself."

"Well?"

50

"Stormfield, don't you see? Her mother knows *cranberries*, and how to tend them, and pick them, and put them up, and market them; and not another blamed thing! Her and her daughter can't be any more company for each other *now* than mud turtle and bird o' paradise. Poor thing, she was looking for a baby to jounce; I think she's struck a disapp'intment."

"Sandy, what will they do — stay unhappy forever in heaven?"

"No, they'll come together and get adjusted by and by. But not this year, and not next. By and by."

Chapter Four

I HAD BEEN HAVING CONSIDERABLE TROUBLE WITH MY WINGS. THE DAY AFTER I HELPED THE CHOIR I MADE A DASH OR TWO WITH them, but was not lucky. First off, I flew thirty yards, and then fouled an Irishman and brought him down—brought us both down, in fact. Next, I had a collision with a Bishop—and bowled him down, of course. We had some sharp words, and I felt pretty cheap, to come banging into a grave old person like that, with a million strangers looking on and smiling to themselves.

I saw I hadn't got the hang of the steering, and so couldn't rightly tell where I was going to bring up when I started. I went afoot the rest of the day, and let my wings hang. Early next morning I went to a private place to have some practice. I got up on a pretty high rock, and got a good start, and went swooping down, aiming for a bush a little over three hundred yards off; but I couldn't seem to calculate for the wind, which was about two points abaft my beam. I could see I was going considerable to looard of the bush, so I worked my starboard wing slow and went ahead strong on the port one, but it wouldn't answer; I could see I was going to broach to, so I slowed down on both, and lit. I went back to the rock and took another chance at it. I aimed two or three points to starboard of the bush—yes, more than that—enough so as to make it nearly a head-wind. I done well enough, but made pretty poor time. I could see, plain enough, that on a head-wind, wings was a mistake. I could see that a body could sail pretty close to the wind, but he couldn't go in the wind's eye. I could see that if I wanted to go a-visiting any distance from home, and the wind was

ahead, I might have to wait days, maybe, for a change; and I could see, too, that these things could not be any use at all in a gale; if you tried to run before the wind, you would make a mess of it, for there isn't any way to shorten sail— like reefing, you know—you have to take it *all* in—shut your feathers down flat to your sides. That would *land* you, of course. You could lay to, with your head to the wind— that is the best you could do, and right hard work you'd find it, too. If you tried any other game, you would founder, sure.

I judge it was about a couple of weeks or so after this that I dropped old Sandy McWilliams a note one day—it was a Tuesday—and asked him to come over and take his manna and quails with me next day; and the first thing he did when he stepped in was to twinkle his eye in a sly way, and say—

"Well, Cap, what you done with your wings?"

I saw in a minute that there was some sarcasm done up in that rag somewheres, but I never let on. I only says—

"Gone to the wash."

"Yes," he says, in a dry sort of way, "they mostly go to the wash—about this time—I've often noticed it. Fresh angels are powerful neat. When do you look for 'em back?"

"Day after to-morrow," says I.

He winked at me, and smiled.

Says I—

"Sandy, out with it. Come—no secrets among friends. I notice you don't ever wear wings—and plenty others don't. I've been making an ass of myself—is that it?"

"That is about the size of it. But it is no harm. We all do it at first. It's perfectly natural. You see, on earth we jump to such foolish conclusions as to things up here. In the pictures we always saw the angels with wings on—and that was all right; but we jumped to the conclusion that that was their way of getting around—and that was all wrong. The wings ain't anything but a uniform, that's all. When they are in the field—so to speak,—they always wear them; you never see an angel going with a message anywhere without his wings, any more than you would see a military

56

officer presiding at a court-martial without his uniform, or a postman delivering letters, or a policeman walking his beat, in plain clothes. But they ain't to *fly* with! The wings are for show, not for use. Old experienced angels are like officers of the regular army—they dress plain, when they are off duty. New angels are like the militia—never shed the uniform—always fluttering and floundering around in their wings, butting people down, flapping here, and there, and everywhere, always imagining they are attracting the admiring eye—well, they just think they are the very most important people in heaven. And when you see one of them come sailing around with one wing tipped up and t'other down, you make up your mind he is saying to himself: ' I wish Mary Ann in Arkansaw could see me now. I reckon she'd wish she hadn't shook me.' No, they're just for show, that's all—only just for show."

"I judge you've got it about right, Sandy," says I.

"Why, look at it yourself," says he. "*You* ain't built for wings—no man is. You know what a grist of years it took you to come here from the earth—and yet you were booming along faster than any cannon-ball could go. Suppose you had to fly that distance with your wings—wouldn't eternity have been over before you got here? Certainly. Well, angels have to go to the earth every day—millions of them—to appear in visions to dying children and good people, you know—it's the heft of their business. They appear with their wings, of course, because they are on official service, and because the dying persons wouldn't know they were angels if they hadn't wings—but do you reckon they fly with them? It stands to reason they don't. The wings

57

would wear out before they got half-way; even the pin-feathers would be gone; the wing frames would be as bare as kite sticks before the paper is pasted on. The distances in heaven are billions of times greater; angels have to go all over heaven every day; could they do it with their wings alone? No, indeed; they wear the wings for style, but they travel any distance in an instant by *wishing*. The wishing-carpet of the Arabian Nights was a sensible idea—but our earthly idea of angels flying these awful distances with their clumsy wings was foolish.

58

"Our young saints, of both sexes, wear wings all the time—blazing red ones, and blue and green, and gold, and variegated, and rainbowed, and ring-streaked-and-striped ones—and nobody finds fault. It is suitable to their time of life. The things are beautiful, and they set the young people off. They are the most striking and lovely part of their outfit—a halo don't *begin.*"

"Well," says I, "I've tucked mine away in the cupboard, and I allow to let them lay there till there's mud."

"Yes—or a reception."

"What's that?"

"Well, you can see one to-night if you want to. There's a barkeeper from Jersey City going to be received."

"Go on—tell me about it."

"This barkeeper got converted at a Moody and Sankey meeting, in New York, and started home on the ferry-boat, and there was a collision and he got drowned. He is of a class that think all heaven goes wild with joy when a particularly hard lot like him is saved; they think all heaven turns out hosannahing to welcome them; they think there isn't anything talked about in the realms of the blest but their case, for that day. This barkeeper thinks there hasn't been such another stir here in years, as his coming is going to raise.—And I've always noticed this peculiarity about a dead barkeeper—he not only expects all hands to turn out when he arrives, but he expects to be received with a torch-light procession."

"I reckon he is disappointed, then."

"No, he isn't. No man is allowed to be disappointed here. Whatever he wants, when he comes—that is, any reasonable and unsacrilegious thing—he can have. There's always a few millions or billions of young folks around who don't want any better entertainment than to fill up their lungs and swarm out with their torches and have a high time over a barkeeper. It tickles the barkeeper till he can't rest, it makes a charming lark for the young folks, it don't do anybody any harm, it don't cost a rap, and it keeps up the place's reputation for making all comers happy and content."

"Very good. I'll be on hand and see them land the barkeeper."

"It is manners to go in full dress. You want to wear your wings, you know, and your other things."

"Which ones?"

"Halo, and harp, and palm branch, and all that."

"Well," says I, "I reckon I ought to be ashamed of myself, but the fact is I left them laying around that day I resigned from the choir. I haven't got a rag to wear but this robe and the wings."

"That's all right. You'll find they've been raked up and saved for you. Send for them."

"I'll do it, Sandy. But what was it you was saying about unsacrilegious things, which people expect to get, and will be disappointed about?"

"Oh, there are a lot of such things that people expect and don't get. For instance, there's a Brooklyn preacher by the name of Talmage, who is laying up a considerable disappointment for himself. He says, every now and then in his sermons, that the first thing he does when he gets to heaven, will be to fling his arms around Abraham, Isaac and Jacob, and kiss them and weep on them. There's millions of people down there on earth that are promising themselves the same thing. As many as sixty thousand people arrive here every single day, that want to run straight to Abraham, Isaac and Jacob, and hug them and weep on them. Now mind you, sixty thousand a day is a prétty heavy contract for those old people. If they were a mind to allow it, they wouldn't ever have anything to do, year in and year out, but stand up and be hugged and wept on thirty-two hours in the twenty-four. They would be tired out and as wét as muskrats all the time. What would heaven be, to *them*? It would be a mighty good place to gét out of—you know that, yourself. Those are kind and gentle old Jews, but they ain't any fonder of kissing the emotional highlights of Brooklyn than you be. You mark my words, Mr. T.'s endearments are going to be declined, with thanks. There are limits to the privileges of the elect, even in heaven. Why, if Adam was to show himself to every new comer that wants to call and gaze at him and strike him for his autograph, he would never have time to do anything else but just that. Talmage has said he is going to give Adam some of his attentions, as well as A., I. and J. But he will have to change his mind about that."

"Do you think Talmage will really come here?"

"Why, certainly, he will; but don't you be alarmed; he will run with his own kind, and there's plenty of them. That is the main charm of heaven—there's all kinds here—which wouldn't be the case if you lét the preachers tell it. Anybody can find the sort he prefers, here, and he just léts the others alone, and they lét him alone. When the Deity builds a heaven, it is built right, and on a liberal plan."

Sandy sent home for his things, and I sent for mine, and about nine in the evening we begun to dress. Sandy says—

"This is going to be a grand time for you, Stormy. Like as not some of the patriarchs will turn out."

"No, but will they?"

"Like as not. Of course they are prétty exclusive. They hardly ever show themselves to the common public. I believe they never turn out except for an eleventh-hour convert. They wouldn't do it then, only earthly tradition makes a grand show prétty necessary on that kind of an occasion."

"Do they all turn out, Sandy?"

"Who?—all the patriarchs? Oh, no—hardly ever more than a couple. You will be here fifty thousand years—maybe more—before you gét a glimpse of all the patriarchs and prophéts. Since I have been here, Job has been to the front once, and once Ham and Jeremiah both at the same time. But the finest thing that has happened in my day was a year or so ago; that was Charles Peace's reception—him they called 'the Bannercross Murderer'—an Englishman. There were four patriarchs and two prophéts on the Grand Stand that time—there hasn't been anything like it since Captain Kidd came; Abel was there—the first time in twelve hundred years. A report got around that Adam was coming; well, of course, Abel was enough to bring a crowd, all by himself, but there is nobody that can draw like Adam. It was a false report, but it got around, anyway, as I say, and it will be a long day before I see the like of it again. The reception was in the English department, of course, which is eight hundred and eleven million miles from the New Jersey line. I went, along with a good many of my neigh-

bors, and it was a sight to see, I can tell you. Flocks came
from all the departments. I saw Esquimaux there, and Tar-
tars, negroes, Chinamen—people from everywhere. You see
a mixture like that in the Grand Choir, the first day you
land here, but you hardly ever see it again. There were billions of people; when they were singing or hosannahing,
the noise was wonderful; and even when their tongues were
still the drumming of the wings was nearly enough to burst
your head, for all the sky was as thick as if it was snowing
angels. Although Adam was not there, it was a great time

anyway, because we had three archangels on the Grand
Stand—it is a seldom thing that even one comes out."

"What did they look like, Sandy?"

"Well, they had shining faces, and shining robes, and
wonderful rainbow wings, and they stood eighteen feet

63

high, and wore swords, and held their heads up in a noble way, and looked like soldiers."

"Did they have halos?"

"No—anyway, not the hoop kind. The archangels and the upper-class patriarchs wear a finer thing than that. It is a round, solid, splendid glory of gold, that is blinding to look at. You have often seen a patriarch in a picture, on earth, with that thing on—you remember it?—he looks as if he had his head in a brass platter. That don't give you the right idea of it at all—it is much more shining and beautiful."

"Did you talk with those archangels and patriarchs, Sandy?"

"Who—I? Why, what can you be thinking about, Stormy? I ain't worthy to speak to such as they."

"Is Talmage?"

"Of course not. You have got the same mixed-up idea about these things that everybody has down there. I had it once, but I got over it. Down there they talk of the heavenly King—and that is right—but then they go right on speaking as if this was a republic and everybody was on a dead level with everybody else, and privileged to fling his arms around anybody he comes across, and be hail-fellow-well-met with all the elect, from the highest down. How tangled up and absurd that is! How are you going to have a republic under a king? How are you going to have a republic at all, where the head of the government is absolute, holds his place forever, and has no parliament, no council to meddle or make in his affairs, nobody voted for, nobody elected, nobody in the whole universe with a voice in the government, nobody asked to take a hand in its matters, and nobody *allowed* to do it? Fine republic, ain't it?"

"Well, yes—it *is* a little different from the idea I had— but I thought I might go around and gét acquainted with the grandees, anyway—not exactly splice the main-brace with them, you know, but shake hands and pass the time of day."

"Could Tom, Dick and Harry call on the Cabinét of Russia and do that?—on Prince Gortschakoff, for instance?"

"I reckon not, Sandy."

"Well, this is Russia—only more so. There's not the shadow of a republic about it anywhere. There are ranks, here. There are viceroys, princes, governors, sub-governors, sub-sub-governors, and a hundred orders of nobility, grading along down from grand-ducal archangels, stage by stage, till the general level is struck, where there ain't any titles. Do you know what a prince of the blood is, on earth?"

"No."

"Well, a prince of the blood don't belong to the royal family exactly, and he don't belong to the mere nobility of the kingdom; he is lower than the one, and higher than t'other. That's about the position of the patriarchs and prophéts here. There's some mighty high nobility here— people that you and I ain't worthy to polish sandals for— and *they* ain't worthy to polish sandals for the patriarchs and prophéts. That gives you a kind of an idea of their rank, don't it? You begin to see how high up they are, don't you? Just to gét a two-minute glimpse of one of them is a thing for a body to remember and tell about for a thousand years. Why, Captain, just think of this: if Abraham was to sét foot down here by this door, there would be a railing sét up

65

around that foot-track right away, and a shelter put over it, and people would flock here from all over heaven, for hundreds and hundreds of years, to look at it. Abraham is one of the parties that Mr. Talmage, of Brooklyn, is going to embrace, and kiss, and weep on, when he comes. He wants to lay in a good stock of tears, you know, or five to one he will go dry before he gets a chance to do it."

"Sandy," says I, "I had an idea that I was going to be equals with everybody here, too, but I will let that drop. It don't matter, and I am plenty happy enough anyway."

"Captain, you are happier than you would be, the other way. These old patriarchs and prophets have got ages the start of you; they know more in two minutes than you know in a year. Did you ever try to have a sociable improving-time discussing winds, and currents and variations of compass with an undertaker?"

"I get your idea, Sandy. He couldn't interest me. He would be an ignoramus in such things—he would bore me, and I would bore him."

"You have got it. You would bore the patriarchs when you talked, and when they talked they would shoot over your head. By and by you would say, 'Good morning, your Eminence, I will call again' —but you wouldn't. Did you ever ask the slush-boy to come up in the cabin and take dinner with you?"

"I get your drift again, Sandy. I wouldn't be used to such grand people as the patriarchs and prophets, and I would be sheepish and tongue-tied in their company, and mighty glad to get out of it. Sandy, which is the highest rank, patriarch or prophet?"

66

"Oh, the prophets hold over the patriarchs. The newest prophet, even, is of a sight more consequence than the oldest patriarch. Yes, sir, Adam himself has to walk behind Shakespeare."

"Was Shakespeare a prophet?"

"Of course he was; and so was Homer, and heaps more. But Shakespeare and the rest have to walk behind a common tailor from Tennessee, by the name of Billings; and behind a horse-doctor named Sakka, from Afghanistan. Jeremiah, and Billings and Buddha walk together, side by side, right behind a crowd from planets not in our astronomy; next come a dozen or two from Jupiter and other worlds; next come Daniel, and Sakka and Confucius; next a lot from systems outside of ours; next come Ezekiel, and Mahomet, Zoroaster, and a knife-grinder from ancient Egypt; then there is a long string, and after them, away down toward the bottom, come Shakespeare and Homer, and a shoemaker named Marais, from the back settlements of France."

"Have they really rung in Mahomet and all those other heathens?"

"Yes—they all had their message, and they all get their reward. The man who don't get his reward on earth, needn't bother—he will get it here, sure."

"But why did they throw off on Shakespeare, that way, and put him away down there below those shoemakers and horse-doctors and knife-grinders—a lot of people nobody ever heard of?"

"That is the heavenly justice of it—they warn't rewarded according to their deserts, on earth, but here they get their rightful rank. That tailor Billings, from Tennessee, wrote

67

poetry that Homer and Shakespeare couldn't begin to come up to; but nobody would print it, nobody read it but his neighbors, an ignorant lot, and they laughed at it. Whenever the village had a drunken frolic and a dance, they would drag him in and crown him with cabbage leaves, and pretend to bow down to him; and one night when he was sick and nearly starved to death, they had him out and crowned him, and then they rode him on a rail about the village, and everybody followed along, beating tin pans and yelling. Well, he died before morning. He wasn't ever expecting to go to heaven, much less that there was going to be any fuss made over him, so I reckon he was a good deal surprised when the reception broke on him."

"Was you there, Sandy?"

"Bless you, no!"

"Why? Didn't you know it was going to come off?"

"Well, I judge I did. It was the talk of these realms—not for a day, like this barkeeper business, but for twenty years before the man died."

"Why the mischief didn't you go, then?"

"Now how you talk! The like of me go meddling around at the reception of a prophet? A mudsill like me trying to push in and help receive an awful grandee like Edward J. Billings? Why, I should have been laughed at for a billion miles around. I shouldn't ever heard the last of it."

"Well, who did go, then?"

"Mighty few people that you and I will ever get a chance to see, Captain. Not a solitary commoner ever has the luck to see a reception of a prophet, I can tell you. All the nobility, and all the patriarchs and prophets—every last one

68

of them—and all the archangels, and all the princes and governors and viceroys, were there,—and *no* small fry—not a single one. And mind you, I'm not talking about only the grandees from *our* world, but the princes and patriarchs and so on from *all* the worlds that shine in our sky, and from billions more that belong in systems upon systems away outside of the one our sun is in. There were some prophets and patriarchs there that ours ain't a circumstance to, for rank and illustriousness and all that. Some were from Jupiter and other worlds in our own system, but the most celebrated were three poets, Saa, Bo and Soof, from great planets in three different and very remote systems. These three names are common and familiar in every nook and corner of heaven, clear from one end of it to the other—fully as well known as the eighty Supreme Archangels, in fact—whereas our Moses, and Adam, and the rest, have not been heard of outside of our world's little corner of heaven, except by a few very learned men scattered here and there—and they always spell their names wrong, and get the performances of one mixed up with the doings of another, and they almost always locate them simply *in our solar system,* and think that is enough without going into little details such as naming the particular world they are from. It is like a learned Hindoo showing off how much he knows by saying Longfellow lives in the United States—as if he lived all over the United States, and as if the country was so small you couldn't throw a brick there without hitting him. Between you and me, it does gravel me, the cool way people from those monster worlds outside our system snub our little world, and even our system. Of course we think a good deal of Jupiter, because our world is only a potato to it, for size; but then there are worlds in other systems that Jupiter isn't even a mustard-seed to — like the planet Goobra, for instance, which you couldn't squeeze inside the orbit of Halley's comet without straining the rivets. Tourists from Goobra (I mean parties that lived and died there — natives) come here, now and then, and inquire about our world, and when they find out it is so little that a streak of lightning can flash clear around it in the eighth of a second, they have to lean up against something to laugh. Then they screw a glass into their eye and go to examining *us*, as if we were a curious kind of foreign bug, or something of that sort. One of them asked me how long our day was; and when I told him it was twelve hours long, as a general thing, he asked me if people where I was from considered it worth while to get up and wash for such a day as that. That is the way with those Goobra people — they can't seem to let a chance go by to throw it in your face that their day is three hundred and twenty-two of our years long. This young snob was just of age — he was six or seven thousand of his days old — say two million of our years — and he had all the puppy airs that belong to that time of life — that turning-point when a person has got over being a boy and yet ain't quite a man exactly. If it had been anywhere else but in heaven, I would have given him a piece of my mind. Well, anyway, Billings had the grandest reception that has been seen in thousands of centuries, and I think it will have a good effect. His name will be carried pretty far, and it will make our system talked about, and maybe our world, too, and raise us in the respect of the general public of heaven. Why, look here — Shakespeare walked backwards

70

before that tailor from Tennessee, and scattered flowers for him to walk on, and Homer stood behind his chair and waited on him at the banquet. Of course that didn't go for much *there*, amongst all those big foreigners from other systems, as they hadn't heard of Shakespeare or Homer either, but it would amount to considerable down there on our little earth if they could know about it. I wish there was something *in* that miserable spiritualism, so we could send them word. That Tennessee village would set up a monument to Billings, then, and his autograph would outsell Satan's. Well, they had grand times at that reception—a small-fry noble from Hoboken told me all about it—Sir Richard Duffer, Baronet."

"What, Sandy, a nobleman from Hoboken? How is that?"

"Easy enough. Duffer kept a sausage-shop and never saved a cent in his life because he used to give all his spare meat to the poor, in a quiet way. Not tramps—no, the other sort—the sort that will starve before they will beg—honest square people out of work. Dick used to watch hungry-looking men and women and children, and track them home, and find out all about them from the neighbors, and then feed them and find them work. As nobody ever *saw* him give anything to anybody, he had the reputation of being mean; he died with it, too, and everybody said it was a good riddance; but the minute he landed here, they made him a baronet, and the very first words Dick the sausage-maker of Hoboken heard when he stepped upon the heavenly shore were, 'Welcome, Sir Richard Duffer!' It surprised him some, because he thought he had reasons to believe he was pointed for a warmer climate than this one."

All of a sudden the whole region fairly rocked under the crash of eleven hundred and one thunder blasts, all let off at once, and Sandy says—

"There, that's for the barkeep."

I jumped up and says—

"Then let's be moving along, Sandy; we don't want to miss any of this thing, you know."

"Keep your seat," he says; "he is only just telegraphed, that is all."

"How?"

"That blast only means that he has been sighted from the signal-station. He is off Sandy Hook. The committees will go down to meet him, now, and escort him in. There will be ceremonies and delays; they won't be coming up the Bay for a considerable time, yet. It is several billion miles away, anyway."

"I could have been a barkeeper and a hard lot just as well as not," says I, remembering the lonesome way I arrived, and how there wasn't any committee nor anything.

"I notice some regret in your voice," says Sandy, "and it is natural enough; but let bygones be bygones; you went according to your lights, and it is too late now to mend the thing."

"No, let it slide, Sandy, I don't mind. But you've got a Sandy Hook *here*, too, have you?"

"We've got everything here, just as it is below. All the States and Territories of the Union, and all the kingdoms of the earth and the islands of the sea are laid out here just as they are on the globe—all the same shape they are down there, and all graded to the relative size, only each State and

74

realm and island is a good many billion times bigger here than it is below. There goes another blast."

"What is that one for?"

"That is only another fort answering the first one. They each fire eleven hundred and one thunder blasts at a single dash—it is the usual salute for an eleventh-hour guest; a hundred for each hour and an extra one for the guest's sex; if it was a woman we would know it by their leaving off the extra gun."

"How do we know there's eleven hundred and one, Sandy, when they all go off at once?—and yĕt we certainly do know."

"Our intelleĉts are a good deal sharpened up, here, in some ways, and that is one of them. Numbers and sizes and distances are so great, here, that we have to be made so we can *feel* them—our old ways of counting and measuring and ciphering wouldn't ever give us an idea of them, but would only confuse us and oppress us and make our heads ache."

After some more talk about this, I says: "Sandy, I notice that I hardly ever see a white angel; where I run across one white angel, I strike as many as a hundred million copper-colored ones—people that can't speak English. How is that?"

"Well, you will find it the same in any State or Territory of the American corner of heaven you choose to go to. I have shot along, a whole week on a strĕtch, and gone millions and millions of miles, through perfeĉt swarms of angels, without ever seeing a single white one, or hearing a word I could understand. You see, America was occupied a billion years and more, by Injuns and Aztecs, and that sort of folks, before a white man ever sĕt his foot in it. During the first three hundred years after Columbus's discovery, there wasn't ever more than one good lecture audience of white people, all put together, in America—I mean the whole thing, British Possessions and all; in the beginning of our century there were only 6,000,000 or 7,000,000—say seven; 12,000,000 or 14,000,000 in 1825; say 23,000,000 in 1850; 40,000,000 in 1875. Our death-rate has always been 20 in 1000 per annum. Well, 140,000 died the first year of the century; 280,000 the twenty-fifth year; 500,000 the fiftieth year; about a million the seventy-fifth year. Now I am going to be liberal about this thing, and consider that fifty million whites have died in America from the beginning up to today—make it sixty, if you want to; make it a hundred million—it's no difference about a few millions one way or t'other. Well, now, you can see, yourself, that when you come to spread a little dab of people like that over these hundreds of billions of miles of American territory here in heaven, it is like scattering a ten-cent box of homeopathic pills over the Great Sahara and expecting to find them again. You can't expect us to amount to anything in heaven, and we *don't*—now that is the simple fact, and we have got to do the best we can with it. The learned men from other planets and other systems come here and hang around a while, when they are touring around the Kingdom, and then go back to their own section of heaven and write a book of travels, and they give America about five lines in it. And what do they say about us? They say this wilderness is populated with a scattering few hundred thousand billions of red angels, with now and then a curiously complected *diseased* one. You see, they think we whites and the occasional

76

nigger are Injuns that have been bleached out or blackened by some leprous disease or other—for some peculiarly rascally *sin*, mind you. It is a mighty sour pill for us all, my friend—even the modestest of us, let alone the other kind, that think they are going to be received like a long-lost government bond, and hug Abraham into the bargain. I haven't asked you any of the particulars, Captain, but I judge it goes without saying—if my experience is worth anything—that there wasn't much of a hooraw made over you when you arrived—now was there?"

"Don't mention it, Sandy," says I, coloring up a little; "I wouldn't have had the family see it for any amount you are a mind to name. Change the subject, Sandy, change the subject."

"Well, do you think of settling in the California department of bliss?"

"I don't know. I wasn't calculating on doing anything really definite in that direction till the family come. I thought I would just look around, meantime, in a quiet way, and make up my mind. Besides, I know a good many dead people, and I was calculating to hunt them up and swap a little gossip with them about friends, and old times, and one thing or another, and ask them how they like it here, as far as they have got. I reckon my wife will want to camp in the California range, though, because most all her departed will be there, and she likes to be with folks she knows."

"Don't you let her. You see what the Jersey district of heaven is, for whites; well, the Californian district is a thousand times worse. It swarms with a mean kind of leather-headed mud-colored angels—and your nearest white neighbor is likely to be a million miles away. *What a man mostly misses, in heaven, is company*—company of his own sort and color and language. I have come near settling in the European part of heaven once or twice on that account."

"Well, why didn't you, Sandy?"

"Oh, various reasons. For one thing, although you *see* plenty of whites there, you can't understand any of them, hardly, and so you go about as hungry for talk as you do here. I like to look at a Russian or a German or an Italian—I even like to look at a Frenchman if I ever have the luck to catch him engaged in anything that ain't indelicate—but *looking* don't cure the hunger—what you want is talk."

"Well, there's England, Sandy—the English district of heaven."

"Yes, but it is not so very much better than this end of the heavenly domain. As long as you run across Englishmen born this side of three hundred years ago, you are all right; but the minute you get back of Elizabéth's time the language begins to fog up, and the further back you go the foggier it gets. I had some talk with one Langland and a man by the name of Chaucer—old-time poéts—but it was no use, I couldn't quite understand them, and they couldn't quite understand me. I have had létters from them since, but it is such broken English I can't make it out. Back of those men's time the English are just simply foreigners, nothing more, nothing less; they talk Danish, German, Norman French, and sometimes a mixture of all three; back of *them*, they talk Latin, and ancient British, Irish, and Gaelic; and then back of these come billions and billions of pure savages that talk a gibberish that Satan himself couldn't understand. The fact is, where you strike one man in the English settlements that you can understand, you wade through awful swarms that talk something you can't make head nor tail of. You see, every country on earth has been overlaid so often, in the course of a billion years, with different kinds of people and different sorts of languages, that this sort of mongrel business was bound to be the result in heaven."

"Sandy," says I, "did you see a good many of the great people history tells about?"

"Yes—plenty. I saw kings and all sorts of distinguished people."

"Do the kings rank just as they did below?"

"No; a body can't bring his rank up here with him. Divine right is a good-enough earthly romance, but it don't go, here. Kings drop down to the general level as soon as they reach the realms of grace. I knew Charles the Second very well—one of the most popular comedians in the English section—draws first rate. There are better, of course—people that were never heard of on earth—but Charles is making a very good reputation indeed, and is considered a rising man. Richard the Lion-hearted is in the prize-ring, and coming into considerable favor. Henry the Eighth is a tragedian, and the scenes where he kills people are done to the very life. Henry the Sixth keeps a religious book stand."

"Did you ever see Napoleon, Sandy?"

"Often—sometimes in the Corsican range, sometimes in the French. He always hunts up a conspicuous place, and goes frowning around with his arms folded and his field-glass under his arm, looking as grand, gloomy and peculiar

79

as his reputation calls for, and very much bothered because he don't stand as high, here, for a soldier, as he expected to."

"Why, who stands higher?"

"Oh, a *lot* of people *we* never heard of before—the shoe-maker and horse-doctor and knife-grinder kind, you know—clodhoppers from goodness knows where, that never handled a sword or fired a shot in their lives—but the soldier-ship was in them, though they never had a chance to show it. But here they take their right place, and Caesar and Napoleon and Alexander have to take a back seat. The greatest military genius our world ever produced was a bricklayer from somewhere back of Boston—died during the Revolution—by the name of Absalom Jones. Wherever he goes, crowds flock to see him. You see, everybody knows that if he had had a chance he would have shown the world some generalship that would have made all generalship before look like child's play and 'prentice work. But he never got a chance; he tried heaps of times to enlist as a private, but he had lost both thumbs and a couple of front teeth, and the recruiting sergeant wouldn't pass him. However, as I say, everybody knows, now, what he *would* have been, and so they flock by the million to get a glimpse of him whenever they hear he is going to be anywhere. Caesar, and Hannibal, and Alexander, and Napoleon are all on his staff, and ever so many more great generals; but the public hardly care to look at *them* when *he* is around. Boom! There goes another salute. The barkeeper's off quarantine now."

Sandy and I put on our things. Then we made a wish, and in a second we were at the reception-place. We stood on the edge of the ocean of space, and looked out over the dimness, but couldn't make out anything. Close by us was the Grand Stand—tier on tier of dim thrones rising up toward the zenith. From each side of it spread away the tiers of seats for the general public. They spread away for leagues and leagues—you couldn't see the ends. They were empty and still, and hadn't a cheerful look, but looked dreary, like a theatre before anybody comes—gas turned down. Sandy says—

"We'll sit down here and wait. We'll see the head of the procession come in sight away off yonder pretty soon, now."

Says I—

"It's pretty lonesome, Sandy; I reckon there's a hitch somewheres. Nobody but just you and me—it ain't much of a display for the barkeeper."

"Don't you fret, it's all right. There'll be one more gun-fire—then you'll see."

In a little while we noticed a sort of a lightish flush, away off on the horizon.

"Head of the torchlight procession," says Sandy.

It spread, and got lighter and brighter: soon it had a strong glare like a locomotive headlight; it kept on getting brighter and brighter till it was like the sun peeping above the horizon-line at sea—the big red rays shot high up into the sky.

"Keep your eyes on the Grand Stand and the miles of seats—sharp!" says Sandy, "and listen for the gunfire."

Just then it burst out, "Boom-boom-boom!" like a million thunderstorms in one, and made the whole heavens rock. Then there was a sudden and awful glare of light all

81

about us, and in that very instant every one of the millions of seats was occupied, and as far as you could see, in both directions, was just a solid pack of people, and the place was all splendidly lit up! It was enough to take a body's breath away. Sandy says—

" That is the way we do it here. No time fooled away; nobody straggling in after the curtain's up. Wishing is quicker work than traveling. A quarter of a second ago these folks were millions of miles from here. When they heard the last signal, all they had to do was to wish, and here they are."

The prodigious choir struck up—

We long to hear thy voice,
To see thee face to face.

It was noble music, but the uneducated chipped in and spoilt it, just as the congregations used to do on earth.

The head of the procession began to pass, now, and it was a wonderful sight. It swept along, thick and solid, five hundred thousand angels abreast, and every angel carrying a torch and singing—the whirring thunder of the wings made a body's head ache. You could follow the line of the procession back, and slanting upward into the sky, far away in a glittering snaky rope, till it was only a faint streak in the distance. The rush went on and on, for a long time, and at last, sure enough, along comes the barkeeper, and then everybody rose, and a cheer went up that made the heavens shake, I tell you! He was all smiles, and had his halo tilted over one ear in a cocky way, and was the most satisfied-

82

looking saint I ever saw. While he marched up the steps of the Grand Stand, the choir struck up—

> The whole wide heaven groans,
> And waits to hear that voice

There were four gorgeous tents standing side by side in the place of honor, on a broad railed platform in the centre of the Grand Stand, with a shining guard of honor round about them. The tents had been shut up all this time. As the barkeeper climbed along up, bowing and smiling to everybody, and at last got to the platform, these tents were jerked up aloft all of a sudden, and we saw four noble thrones of gold, all caked with jewels, and in the two middle ones sat old white-whiskered men, and in the two others a couple of the most glorious and gaudy giants, with platter halos and beautiful armor. All the millions went down on their knees, and stared, and looked glad, and burst out into a joyful kind of murmurs. They said—

"Two archangels!—that is splendid. Who can the others be?"

The archangels gave the barkeeper a stiff little military bow; the two old men rose; one of them said, "Moses and Esau welcome thee!" and then all the four vanished, and the thrones were empty.

The barkeeper looked a little disappointed, for he was calculating to hug those old people, I judge; but it was the gladdest and proudest multitude you ever saw—because they had seen Moses and Esau. Everybody was saying, "Did

83

you see them?—I did—Esau's side face was to me, but I saw Moses full in the face, just as plain as I see you this minute."

The procession took up the barkeeper and moved on with him again, and the crowd broke up and scattered. As we went along home, Sandy said it was a great success, and the barkeeper would have a right to be proud of it forever. And he said *we* were in luck, too; said we might attend receptions for forty thousand years to come, and not have a chance to see a brace of such grand moguls as Moses and Esau. We found afterwards that we had come near seeing another patriarch, and likewise a genuine prophet besides, but at the last moment they sent regrets. Sandy said there would be a monument put up there, where Moses and Esau had stood, with the date and circumstances, and all about the whole business, and travelers would come for thousands of years and gawk at it, and climb over it, and scribble their names on it.

Part Two ✢
Letter from the Recording Angel

Andrew Langdon
Coal Dealer
Buffalo, New York

I Have the honor, as per command, to inform you that your recent act of benevolence and self-sacrifice has been recorded upon a page of the Book called *Golden Deeds of Men*: a distinction, I am permitted to remark, which is not merely extraordinary, it is unique.

As regards your prayers, for the week ending the 19th, I have the honor to report as follows:

1. For weather to advance hard coal 15 cents a ton. Granted.

2. For influx of laborers to reduce wages 10 per cent. Granted.

3. For a break in rival soft-coal prices. Granted.

4. For a visitation upon the man, or upon the family of the man, who has set up a competing retail coal-yard in Rochester. Granted, as follows: diphtheria, 2, 1 fatal; scarlet fever, 1, to result in deafness and imbecility. Note. This prayer should have been directed against this subordinate's principals, The N. Y. Central R. R. Co.

5. For deportation to Sheol of annoying swarms of persons who apply daily for work, or for favors of one sort or another. Taken under advisement for later decision and

compromise, this petition appearing to conflict with another one of same date, which will be cited further along.

6. For application of some form of violent death to neighbor who threw brick at family cat, whilst the same was

serenading. Reserved for consideration and compromise because of conflict with a prayer of even date to be cited further along.

7. To "damn the missionary cause." Reserved also—as above.

8. To increase December profits of $22,230 to $45,000 for January, and perpetuate a proportionate monthly increase thereafter—"which will satisfy you." The prayer granted; the added remark accepted with reservations.

9. For cyclone, to destroy the works and fill up the mine of the North Pennsylvania Co. NOTE: Cyclones are not kept in stock in the winter season. A reliable article of fire-damp can be furnished upon application.

Especial note is made of the above list, they being of

particular moment. The 298 remaining supplications classifiable under the head of Special Providences, Schedule A, for the week ending 19th, are granted in a body, except that 3 of the 32 cases requiring immediate death have been modified to incurable disease.

This completes the week's invoice of petitions known to this office under the technical designation of Secret Supplications of the Heart, and which for a reason which may suggest itself, always receive our first and especial attention.

The remainder of the week's invoice falls under the head of what we term Public Prayers, in which classification we place prayers uttered in Prayer Meeting, Sunday School, Class Meeting, Family Worship, &c. These kinds of prayers have value according to classification of Christian uttering them. By rule of this office, Christians are divided into two grand classes, to wit: 1, Professing Christians; 2, Professional Christians. These, in turn, are minutely subdivided and classified by size, species, and family; and finally, standing is determined by carats, the minimum being 1, the maximum 1,000.

As per balance-sheet for quarter ending Dec. 31, 1847, you stood classified as follows:

Grand Classification, Professing Christian.

Size, one-fourth of maximum.

Species, Human-Spiritual.

Family, A of the Elect, Division 16.

Standing, 322 carats fine.

As per balance-sheet for quarter just ended—that is to say, forty years later—you stand classified as follows:

Grand Classification, Professional Christian.

Size, six one-hundredths of maximum.

Species, Human-Animal.

Family, W of the Elect, Division 1547.

Standing, 3 carats fine.

I have the honor to call your attention to the fact that you seem to have deteriorated.

To resume report upon your Public Prayers—with the side remark that in order to encourage Christians of your grade and of approximate grades, it is the custom of this office to grant many things to them which would not be granted to Christians of a higher grade—partly because they would not be asked for:

Prayer for weather mercifully tempered to the needs of the poor and the naked. Denied. This was a Prayer-Meeting Prayer. It conflicts with Item 1 of this report, which was a Secret Supplication of the Heart. By a rigid rule of this office, certain sorts of Public Prayers of Professional Christians are forbidden to take precedence of Secret Supplications of the Heart.

Prayer for better times and plentier food "for the hard-handed son of toil whose patient and exhausting labors make comfortable the homes, and pleasant the ways, of the more fortunate, and entitle him to our vigilant and effective protection from the wrongs and injustices which grasping avarice would do him, and to the tenderest offices of our grateful hearts." Prayer-Meeting Prayer. Refused. Conflicts with Secret Supplication of the Heart No. 2.

Prayer "that such as in any way obstruct our preferences may be generously blessed, both themselves and their families, we here calling our hearts to witness that in their

90

worldly prosperity we are spiritually blessed, and our joys made perfect." Prayer-Meeting Prayer. Refused. Conflicts with Secret Supplications of the Heart Nos. 3 and 4.

"Oh, let none fall heir to the pains of perdition through words or acts of ours." Family Worship. Received fifteen minutes in advance of Secret Supplication of the Heart No. 5, with which it distinctly conflicts. It is suggested that one or the other of these prayers be withdrawn, or both of them modified.

"Be mercifully inclined toward all who would do us offense in our persons or our property." Includes man who threw brick at cat. Family Prayer. Received some minutes in advance of No. 6, Secret Supplications of the Heart. Modification suggested, to reconcile discrepancy.

"Grant that the noble missionary cause, the most precious labor entrusted to the hands of men, may spread and prosper without let or limit in all heathen lands that do as yet reproach us with their spiritual darkness." Uninvited prayer shoved in at meeting of American Board. Received nearly half a day in advance of No. 7, Secret Supplications of the Heart. This office takes no stock in missionaries, and is not connected in any way with the American Board. We should like to grant one of these prayers but cannot grant both. It is suggested that the American Board one be withdrawn.

This office desires for the twentieth time to call urgent attention to your remark appended to No. 8. It is a chestnut.

Of the 464 specifications contained in your Public Prayers for the week, and not previously noted in this report, we grant 2, and deny the rest. To wit: Granted, (1), "that the clouds may continue to perform their office; (2), and the sun his." It was the divine purpose anyhow; it will gratify you to know that you have not disturbed it. Of the 462 details refused, 61 were uttered in Sunday School. In this connection I must once more remind you that we grant no Sunday School Prayers of Professional Christians of the classification technically known in this office as the John Wanamaker grade. We merely enter them as "words," and they count to his credit according to number uttered within certain limits of time; 3,000 per quarter-minute required, or no score; 4,200 in a possible 5,000 is a quite common Sunday School score among experts, and counts the same as two hymns and a bouquet furnished by young ladies in the assassin's cell, execution-morning. Your remaining 401 details count for wind only. We bunch them and use them for head-winds in retarding the ships of improper people, but it takes so many of them to make an impression that we cannot allow anything for their use.

I desire to add a word of my own to this report. When certain sorts of people do a sizable good deed, we credit them up a thousand-fold more for it than we would in the case of a better man—on account of the strain. You stand far away above your classification-record here, because of certain self-sacrifices of yours which greatly exceed what could have been expected of you. Years ago, when you were worth only $100,000, and sent $2 to your impoverished cousin the widow when she appealed to you for help, there were many in heaven who were not able to believe it, and many more who believed that the money was counterfeit. Your character went up many degrees when it was shown that these

92

suspicions were unfounded. A year or two later, when you sent the poor girl $4 in answer to another appeal, everybody believed it, and you were the talk here for days together. Two years later you sent $6, upon supplication, when the widow's youngest child died, and that act made perfect your good fame. Everybody in heaven said, "Have you heard about Andrew?" — for you are now affectionately called Andrew here. Your increasing donation, every two or three years, has kept your name on all lips, and warm in all hearts. All heaven watches you Sundays, as you drive to church in your handsome carriage; and when your hand retires from the contribution plate, the glad shout is heard even to the ruddy walls of remote Sheol, "Another nickel from Andrew!"

But the climax came a few days ago, when the widow wrote and said she could get a school in a far village to teach if she had $50 to get herself and her two surviving children over the long journey; and you counted up last month's clear profit from your three coal mines—$22,230—and added to it the certain profit for the current month—$45,000 and a possible fifty—and then got down your pen and your check-book and mailed her *fifteen whole dollars!* Ah, Heaven bless and keep you forever and ever, generous heart! There was not a dry eye in the realms of bliss; and amidst the hand-shakings, and embracings, and praisings, the decree was thundered forth from the shining mount, that this deed should out-honor all the historic self-sacrifices of men and angels, and be recorded by itself upon a page of its own, for that the strain of it upon you had been heavier and bitterer than the strain it costs ten thousand martyrs to yield up their lives at the fiery stake; and all said, "What is the giving

93

up of life, to a noble soul, or to ten thousand noble souls, compared with the giving up of fifteen dollars out of the greedy grip of the meanest white man that ever lived on the face of the earth?"

And it was a true word. And Abraham, weeping, shook out the contents of his bosom and pasted the eloquent label there, "RESERVED"; and Peter, weeping, said, "He shall be received with a torchlight procession when he comes"; and then all heaven boomed, and was glad you were going there. And so was hell.

[Signed]

THE RECORDING ANGEL [Seal]

By command.

❡ Set by hand in Weiss type by Arthur and Edna Rushmore at The Golden Hind Press in Madison New Jersey. Published by Harper & Brothers in New York in the fall of 1952.